I'M YOUR DAUGHTER, JULIE

Caring for a Parent with Dementia

Julie A. Gorges

Julie A. Gorges
Visit my website at www.juliegorges.com

Printed in the United States of America

First Printing: March 2019
I-Form Ink Publishing

ISBN: 978-0-9763274-7-9
Library of Congress Control Number: 2018911858

For my mother who courageously fought a cruel and merciless disease. Her endless love, generosity, dedication to family, kindness, support, compassion, thoughtfulness, and adventurous spirit displayed throughout her lifetime will not be forgotten.

This book is also dedicated to the 15 million selfless and noble unpaid caregivers of loved ones suffering with Alzheimer's, Lewy body dementia, and other kinds of dementia – the majority of which are family members.

You are the unsung heroes.

ABOUT THE AUTHOR

Julie A. Gorges is the co-author of a non-fiction book and author of two young adult novels. She won three journalism awards and is a blogger at *Baby Boomer Bliss*, recently recognized as one of the top baby boomer blogs on the web. Julie's work has appeared in dozens of national magazines including *Woman's World*, *True Romance*, and *Cricket*.

During her mother's final years of life suffering from Lewy body dementia, Julie was a full-time caregiver.

OTHER BOOKS BY JULIE A. GORGES

FICTION

Just Call Me Goody-Two-Shoes

Time to Cast Away

NON-FICTION

Residential Steel Design and Construction

PRAISE FOR
I'M YOUR DAUGHTER, JULIE

"The most powerful advice for caregivers comes from someone standing in their shoes, seeing what they see and sharing the same struggles. Such an informed and empathetic voice runs through Julie Gorges' book, *I'm Your Daughter, Julie*. It's the ultimate user-friendly guide to caring for someone with dementia, written by a loving daughter who truly understands how to provide the best care."
Marc Agronin, MD, geriatric psychiatrist and author of *The End of Old Age: Living a Longer, More Purposeful Life and The Dementia Caregiver: A Guide to Caring for Someone with Alzheimer's Disease and Other Neurocognitive Disorders.*

"*I'm Your Daughter Julie: Caring for a Parent with Dementia* details the dementia journey from diagnosis to death and beyond. The author shares practical information on caring for a parent with dementia, and details the importance of self-care for the caregiver, leaving the reader with a sense that, while there is no denying how difficult the journey may be, it is navigable. This book is really best described as a well-written guidebook with compact sections within chapters that make easy reading for caregivers when time is short and the stresses of life are long. A 'must read' for anyone entering into the realm of dementia caregiving."
Vicki Tapia, author of *Somebody Stole My Iron: A Family Memoir of Dementia*

"*I'm Your Daughter, Julie* provides a wealth of information for those beginning the journey of caring for a parent with dementia. The material can also apply to a parent or other loved one, who may not have dementia, but is quickly failing in health, when trying to learn the ropes of caregiving quickly can be a challenge. The author includes her own struggles at the end of the book when dealing with her mother's imminent death. Sharing those heartbreaking feelings will benefit family caregivers as they try to prepare for the roller-coaster of emotions that lie ahead. This book is a valuable guidebook to help those needing this type of support and encouragement through a difficult and challenging time."
Cindy Childress, family caregiver for a step-father with dementia

"Thank you, Julie Gorges, for writing this wonderful guidebook for those whose lives and families are affected by all dementias, based upon your personal experience caring for your Mom through Lewy Body."

Jean Lee, author of *Alzheimer's Daughter*

"As a caregiver who has worked with dementia patients, I can relate to Julie Gorges' journey in caring for her mother. Her book brings out, in a loving way, how to cope with the challenges of caring for a loved one with dementia. She expresses herself honestly and I appreciated her research on the subject, which will help families understand what they are dealing with. *I'm Your Daughter, Julie* is very informative and easy-to-read."

Reina Hernandez, professional caregiver

CONTENTS

INTRODUCTION

My Story

My mother suffered from Lewy body dementia (LBD), a cruel combination of Alzheimer's and Parkinson's symptoms that rendered her helpless both physically and mentally toward the end of her life.

LBD is known for tormenting its victims with vivid hallucinations, delusions, and night terrors. Sometimes my mother was in a complete state of panic because she thought a bear was in the laundry room, a tiger was swimming in the pool, or baby lions were squirming in the bottom of her bed.

One time, Mom became hysterical because she saw her long dead step-father – a former boxer who physically abused her mother – standing in the hallway.

Watching Mom slowly lose her mind became a normal part of my life as her full-time caregiver. Sacrificing part of my life to care for a parent with dementia who I loved dearly was one of the best things I've ever accomplished. Caregiving was also the most challenging, demanding, and heartbreaking task I've ever undertaken.

Dementia not only changed my mother forever, it changed me in profound ways too.

I had never heard of this brutal disease before Mom's diagnosis. However, LBD is not rare. According to the Lewy Body Dementia Association (LBDA) and the Mayo Clinic, it is the second most common type of dementia after Alzheimer's. Thankfully, more people have become aware of this disease after it was discovered that actor and comedian Robin Williams suffered from LBD at the time of his death. Recently, CNN founder Ted Turner was also diagnosed with this disease.

Still, much remains to be done to raise awareness. As LBDA's site points out, although LBD affects an estimated 1.4 million individuals and their families in the United States alone, it is currently widely underdiagnosed. Although "many families are affected by this disease, few individuals and medical professionals are aware of the symptoms, diagnostic criteria, or even that LBD exists," their site points out.

This certainly described me. When I began this journey with my mother, I had no idea what ordeal lay ahead. Dementia starts out in a seemingly non-threatening way with some memory loss and confusion. Even as the disease progressed, Mom had some good days when she wasn't as confused, shuffled and trembled less, held her head a bit higher, and was more lucid and alert. Sometimes she'd go days without any hallucinations. This is typical for people with LBD whose symptoms often fluctuate drastically from day to day.

On good days, for a moment of denial, I could pretend she would get better. In fact, this is a belief my Mom often vocalized. "When I get better, it won't be so hard," she'd say optimistically to comfort me, as was her nature.

This statement always caused a pang of distress because I knew deep down that it wasn't true.

As the disease took its inevitable path, I was often hit with that harsh reality. Mom knew who I was most the time. But then there would be days she thought I was a nurse or a professional caretaker and begin making friendly, polite small talk. One day she asked if I liked to sail.

"Yes, Mom," I answered. "You know I love sailing. I'm your daughter, Julie."

Our family has sailed for more than 30 years, so the question was unsettling. After she got sick, Mom would bravely maneuver down the docks with her walker and step into the boat flanked by family members on both sides until she was physically unable to do so. Everyone on the dock admired her for that.

"Oh yeah, I know you're Julie," she said, looking a little embarrassed.

A few moments later, she asked the name of my mother as if I were a stranger again. Trying to have a sense of humor, I said her name, Carmen Hacker. She looked confused and I felt bad.

"You're my mother," I explained sadly. "I'm your daughter, Julie."

My Mom often told me about something I did in the past as if explaining an incident to a stranger.

"My Julie..." she'd begin the story and relate something that happened in my childhood. Or she would say, "My Julie takes good care of me."

Her appreciation warmed my heart and made all the sacrifices seem worthwhile. At the same time, it broke my heart because my mother didn't recognize me when she said it.

We tried to laugh at those moments when my Mom's mind would come back, but painfully, deep down, I knew we'd been given a disturbing glimpse into the future. The day would come when my mother wouldn't recognize me at all. Even though I would patiently explain who I was, she wouldn't understand anymore.

LOSING A PARENT, A LITTLE BIT AT A TIME

Sometimes you lose a parent in death suddenly. What you don't realize until you have a parent with dementia is that sometimes you lose a parent excruciatingly – a little bit at a time. Grief takes many forms and it isn't just for mourning someone who has died.

After my Mom lost her ruthless battle with LBD, many people encouraged me, as an author and professional writer, to pen a book to share my experiences and offer advice to other caregivers.

Although I had shared some of my story in my blog, *Baby Boomer Bliss*, I couldn't immediately dive into an entire book on the subject. The heartbreaking experience of watching my Mom rapidly deteriorate both physically and mentally before my eyes, the difficulty of taking care of her at the end when she began to lose all bodily functions, as well as her death were all too painful to relive.

Telling my story still isn't easy, but I've finally healed enough to put my feelings into words. I hope that my experiences, my successes, and my mistakes can help all you dear caregivers.

This book is a memoir of sorts sharing my intimate story, but it is also a practical guidebook. I want to help you cope with the many challenges that lie ahead, learn how to take care of yourself during this difficult time, and succeed with your noble and important role as a caregiver. By sharing my journey with you, I want to make the process a bit easier and provide some comfort to all of you who are losing your loved one a little bit at a time like I did.

Although this book is written specifically for those caring for a parent with dementia, it is also valuable for caregivers of spouses, relatives, or friends suffering with this disease. The information is meant to help you whether you're a full-time caregiver, helping another family member or friend on a part-time basis, or looking after a parent who is living in an assisted living facility or nursing home. In fact, much of the book applies to caregiving in general, no matter what disease or disability your loved one may have.

To be clear, I'm not a health professional writing this book from a medical standpoint. Although I'll briefly go over some of the different kinds of dementia along with general symptoms, so you'll know what to expect, this is a deeply personal book written from my heart.

I'm reaching out to you as one who has traveled this difficult but, in the end, worthwhile journey you are already on or ready to embark. You'll notice the book is short and to the point because I know from personal experience that as a caregiver your time is limited.

THE FACTS AND FIGURES

If you're caring for a parent with dementia, you are certainly not alone. The statistics are brutal. Shockingly, one in three seniors dies with Alzheimer's or another form of dementia.

According to the Alzheimer's Association, about 15 million adult family caregivers care for someone who has Alzheimer's disease or another kind of dementia. They provide an estimated 17.7 billion hours of unpaid care valued at more than $220 billion.

The truth is that while the government spends an estimated $150 billion annually with Medicaid and Medicare to care for those with dementia and about $570 million on drug research to cure or slow the onset of Alzheimer's disease, it does little to support those family caregivers whose loved ones suffer from dementia. Sadly, very few programs pay family members or friends on a regular basis to provide care.

Nearly 10 million people caring for aging parents are over the age of 50, according to a study conducted by the MetLife Mature Market Institute. Because life expectancy has increased during this past century, the number of caregivers has more than tripled over the past 15 years and it's not unusual for retirees over the age of 65 to be caring for a parent. Most, but not all, caregivers are married, employed women.

Nearly half of family caregivers surveyed by The Home Alone said they performed medical and nursing tasks. More than 96% also helped their loved one with daily activities such as personal hygiene, dressing/undressing, getting in and out of bed, giving prescribed medications, shopping for groceries, and providing transportation. According to one Gallup poll, the majority of respondents had been caregiving for three years or more.

"Without caregivers, people with dementia would have a poorer quality of life and would need institutional care more quickly, and national economies would be swept away by the advancing demographic tidal wave," a report from The National Center for Biotechnology Information (NCBI) states. The report adds that this support comes at a cost of caregiver distress.

Indeed, caring for a loved one with dementia takes an emotional toll. According to the Family Caregiver Alliance (FCA), a person who provides care for someone with dementia is twice as likely to suffer from depression as a person providing care for someone without dementia.

That's because caring for a person with dementia presents extra challenges. "Dementia-related symptoms such as wandering, agitation, hoarding, embarrassing conduct, and resistance or non-cooperation from the loved one makes every day challenging and makes it harder for a caregiver to get rest or assistance in providing care," FCA's website points out. "The more severe the case of dementia, the more likely the caregiver is to experience depression."

Other emotions are involved as well. Even the most capable and responsible caregivers can feel overwhelmed, anxious, frustrated, isolated, and exhausted – on top of feeling guilty for having these feelings.

PROS AND CONS OF CAREGIVING

My personal story matches many of the statistics I've listed above. I won't sugarcoat this. Caregiving for someone with dementia is one of the most difficult jobs you'll ever encounter. All the patience, courage, strength, and compassion you can muster will be needed. I say this even though I had a lot of support from my family. Not everyone has this kind of backing.

But I want to add that caregiving is a life-changing experience that is fulfilling and inspiring as well as difficult and painful. Essentially, you're giving up part of your life to take care of someone you love during his or her darkest hours. That is certainly a worthwhile objective. For that reason, you'll feel a sense of accomplishment at the end of this difficult road.

Like many adult children, I had assured my mother repeatedly that she'd never be put in a nursing home, which was her biggest fear. Motivated by my intense love for her and a strong religious belief that children should care for their parents, I kept that promise. But to be perfectly honest, some days I didn't know if I could continue for another minute.

Caring for someone with dementia is physically, mentally, and emotionally draining. In fact, if you're unable to provide full-time caregiving for your loved one, don't feel guilty. Our family ended up hiring in-home full-time professional help at the end of Mom's life, but I wish we had done so sooner. By that time, I was experiencing symptoms of caregiver burnout. In Chapter 9, I discuss all the many options available to caregivers today whether you need part- or full-time help.

But here's the thing for all of you who, like me, choose to take this path despite the tremendous challenges and sacrifices. Caregiving is a labor of love.

Taking care of my Mom allowed me to connect with her on a deeply emotional level. It was a once-in-a-lifetime chance to give my mother the same kind of loving care she unselfishly gave me throughout her life. It was an opportunity to make the end of my Mom's life as comfortable as possible in a loving atmosphere. I had to remind myself often of the reasons I undertook this task to overcome the anguish that comes with the territory. If you choose this course, you'll need to do the same.

No doubt, the personal growth and life lessons experienced on this journey made me a better person. I've always been religious, but my faith was strengthened as I learned to rely on God like never before. During difficult moments, I found an inner strength, fortitude, and resilience that I didn't know were there that makes me more confident about overcoming any future challenges. The experience also made me more empathetic and compassionate – not only toward other caregivers – but people facing all kinds of struggles and trials.

Caregiving can be a worthwhile experience, but only if you're providing care for the right reasons. Your motives cannot be based purely on guilt, a reluctant sense of duty, or – even worse – performed with an eye on inheritance. The report from NCBI referenced earlier adds that caregivers with the wrong incentives are "more likely to resent their role and suffer greater physiological distress than caregivers with more positive motivations."

If you had a difficult relationship with your parent in the past, determine if you're able to overcome the complex feelings involved to become a caregiver. Maybe your father abandoned or neglected you as a child and has come back because he needs care. Or your unkind and critical mother expects you to care for her. Some adult children can overcome their feelings to become a caregiver while others decide it's too painful and investigate other options.

While I realize not everyone has a good relationship with their parents, this was not the case with my mother. She was my best friend and I loved her desperately. We were in this together – better or worse – to the very end. While I'm proud that I gave caregiving everything I had, could I have done better? Oh, yes. That's one of the reasons I'm writing this book. I want to help you avoid some of my many mistakes.

LEARNING FROM MY MISTAKES

Let's get real. Like many who care for family members, I was unprepared, inexperienced, and untrained when I was thrust into the role of full-time caregiving. Most of us are not nurses or professional caregivers.

At first, I didn't know what to expect as the disease progressed. What was the best treatment? How could I communicate with my Mom when she became difficult and irrational? Many of the physical tasks also puzzled me such as how to lift my Mom from a chair or help her get dressed.

Unlike a professional caregiver, I was caring for my own mother which was complicated emotionally. I was by no means prepared for the strong fluctuating feelings that shifted wildly from day to day.

My emotions ranged from a yearning for the mother I once knew and loved, to anger and frustration with the inevitable and relentless progress of this disease, to helplessness as I watched symptoms worsen, to guilt when I lost my patience, to fear and worry of what lie ahead, to a deep and profound sadness.

During my lifetime, I relied heavily on my mother for advice, guidance, friendship, and support. Now, I had to adjust to her being totally dependent on me. I was mourning the loss of the mother I knew and trying to accept and love the person she had become.

I also grieved for the freedom I once took for granted. Although other family members gave me regular breaks, I could no longer leave the house without a "babysitter." Often, I felt hopelessly trapped. Fortunately, as a freelance writer, I could work from home, but writing takes concentration and the constant interruptions and demands were frustrating. Eventually, I had to give up most of my larger clients.

Even though my Mom displayed childlike traits caused by her disease, she clearly was not a kid and deserved to be treated with respect and dignity. This made caregiving more difficult and confusing than caring for my children when they were young.

Prior to her disease, Mom always served herself last and patiently waited for what she wanted. As the dementia progressed, however, when my mother wanted something, she wanted it NOW like a toddler. Suddenly, my Mom preferred kid's movies like *Free Willy* and children's TV shows like *Full House*. As the disease progressed, she became increasingly stubborn and obstinate like a rebellious teenager.

At the same time, my mother was still an adult with decades of wisdom, experience, and independence behind her. I had to constantly remind myself that this wasn't easy for her either. Most the time, I succeeded in treating her respectfully like an adult, but sadly, not always. When I failed, an enormous amount of guilt and remorse followed.

Sometimes, all these intense emotions overwhelmed me. Sometimes, I felt downright resentful. Sometimes, Mom and I bickered over stupid stuff. Sometimes, I was irritable instead of patient. Sometimes, I thought I would lose my mind along with my mother. Not pretty, but there it is.

My guilty list of "should haves" is long. I should have gotten an accurate diagnosis sooner. I should have been calmer when Mom was unreasonable. While Mom was in a rehabilitation center after surgery, I should have made sure the staff was checking for bedsores. Suffering from burnout, I should have gotten professional help sooner.

Although I tortured myself with all the "should haves" after Mom's death, now that time has passed, I know deep in my heart that I did the best I could under the circumstances. If you decide to be a full-time caregiver for your parent, don't beat yourself up if you're not perfect. From talking to other caregivers and reading books and articles on the subject, I realize mistakes, frustrations, and struggles are part of the bargain.

However, it is my dearest hope that I can help you avoid making some of my mistakes. For example, by sharing how I handled all the emotions that come with this territory – and how I could have dealt with them better in hindsight – I hope you'll be better able to cope with the emotional rollercoaster that lies ahead.

Along this journey, I learned about the different stages of dementia, available treatments, proper transferring techniques, how to improve communications, and ways to deal with disturbing behavioral changes. No less important, I discovered how to care for myself during this challenging time. These are just some of the topics I plan to tackle in this book.

THE END OF THE JOURNEY

Unlike some books on this subject, I'll walk you through the entire process and take you to the end of the journey. By that, I mean that I'll include information that will help you cope after your loved one dies.

When my Mom was first diagnosed, I didn't want to accept that dementia is a fatal disease. As I mentioned before, early stages of dementia often start with memory problems which may seem somewhat insignificant. But I want you to be prepared.

Alzheimer's, LBD, and other forms of dementia are diseases that progress over time and eventually lead to death. Life expectancy depends on age, severity of symptoms, and other medical conditions. However, on average, Alzheimer's patients live between eight to 10 years and LBD patients between five to eight years *after* diagnosis. Consider that these diseases can go undiagnosed for months or even years.

Some with late-stage dementia die of a medical complication, such as pneumonia or some other infection. Others die from a fall as immobility issues arise. However, dementia itself can be lethal. Weight loss, malnutrition, swallowing difficulties, and dehydration are serious risks as the disease progresses.

If you prefer – and I would recommend this – read my final chapters after your loved one passes. When you're ready, I want to share ways you can heal, reinvent yourself, and move forward to live a fulfilling and happy life.

Stay with me and we'll get through this together.

But first, let's start with the basics. What exactly is dementia, what are some of the early warning signs, how is it diagnosed, and what kind of treatments are available? The next section will answer these questions.

SECTION ONE: DEFINING, DIAGNOSING, AND TREATING DEMENTIA

CHAPTER ONE

Types of Dementia

N o matter what type of dementia is involved, knowledge is power. Become informed. You'll be better prepared to handle the wide variety of challenges that lie ahead if you know what to expect.

I'll provide basic information in this chapter but try and learn everything you can about the disease from your doctors, websites, books, and support groups. Once you become informed, you may need to help educate other family members and friends.

So, exactly what is dementia?

DEFINING DEMENTIA

Put simply, I learned that dementia is not a single disease. The word "dementia" is a blanket term that describes symptoms that affect memory, judgment, language, and motor skills.

Dementia is more prevalent among aging people than you may realize. As I mentioned earlier, about one-third of individuals aged 65 years and older develop at least one form of dementia by the time they die.

Many people use the term "Alzheimer's" to describe any type of dementia, which is not accurate. Alzheimer's is the most common type of dementia, but by no means the only kind.

The three most common types of dementia include:

ALZHEIMER'S

Alzheimer's disease accounts for 60 to 80 percent of dementia cases. According to the Alzheimer's Association: "Two abnormal structures called plaques and tangles are prime suspects in damaging and killing nerve cells." This disease gradually leads to intellectual impairment that progresses from forgetfulness to complete disability.

Alzheimer's is the sixth-leading cause of death in the United States and the only cause of death among the top 10 that cannot be prevented, cured, or even slowed down. Early signs include memory and vocabulary problems, confusion, disorientation, and poor judgement. You may notice that your parent has trouble remembering recent conversations, names, or events. Or struggles with normal daily tasks like walking to a familiar place, playing a card game, or comprehending the passage of time.

Early behavior and personality changes include irritability, anxiety, depression, and fatigue.

In later stages, those with Alzheimer's often have difficulty speaking, swallowing, and walking. Behavior problems worsen as the disease progresses and can include agitation, restlessness, sleep disturbances, urinary incontinence, emotional distress, delusions, anger, paranoia, as well as verbal or physical outbursts.

LEWY BODY DEMENTIA (LBD)

Although not as common as Alzheimer's, as mentioned earlier, LBD affects about 1.4 million individuals and their families in the United States.

According to Lewy Body Dementia Association's site, "LBD is a progressive brain disorder in which Lewy bodies (abnormal deposits of a protein called alpha-synuclein) build up in areas of the brain that regulate behavior, cognition, and movement." The site also points out that LBD is an umbrella term for two closely related diagnoses: Parkinson's disease dementia and dementia with Lewy bodies (DLB).

Some of the symptoms, such as memory problems, confusion, difficulty concentrating, disorientation, paranoia, vocabulary problems, agitation, emotional distress, urinary incontinence, anxiety, and depression are like Alzheimer's. Still, there are differences.

Physical deterioration usually occurs more quickly in those with LBD and includes Parkinson-like symptoms such as tremors, lack of motor skills, rigid muscles, difficulty walking, stooped posture, and balance problems. LBD patients are also typically plagued with frequent, intense, and vivid hallucinations as well as disrupted sleep and night terrors during early stages of the disease. Alzheimer's patients usually experience delusions and hallucinations only occasionally during later stages.

While memory problems due to Alzheimer's tend to decline with time, symptoms of LBD vary drastically from day to day. Therefore, a person with LBD may know who you are one day and not recognize you the next.

Those with LBD also tend to be extremely sensitive to certain kinds of medication which can worsen symptoms drastically.

VASCULAR

Vascular dementia accounts for about 10 percent of dementia cases, according to the Alzheimer's Association, and is a result of brain injuries and inadequate blood flow.

Symptoms can vary widely, depending on the severity of the blood vessel damage and the part of the brain affected. Unlike Alzheimer's and LBD, memory loss may or may not be a significant symptom depending on the specific brain areas where blood flow is reduced.

Common symptoms include confusion, disorientation, speech problems, vision loss, and a lack of ability to make decisions or plans. Other noticeable changes can include poor hygiene, compulsive behavior, and lack of motivation. Vascular dementia symptoms may be most obvious after a major stroke.

OTHER TYPES OF DEMENTIA

Other dementia diseases are less common and include:
- Frontotemporal dementia known for changes in personality and behavior and difficulty with language.
- Creutzfeldt-Jakob disease, a rare, fatal brain disorder that impairs memory and coordination and causes behavior changes.

- Normal pressure hydrocephalus with symptoms that include difficulty walking, memory loss and inability to control urination.
- Huntington's disease known for abnormal involuntary movements, a severe decline in thinking and reasoning skills, and irritability, depression and other mood changes.
- Wernicke-Korsakoff syndrome recognized for its severe memory problems often connected to alcohol misuse.

MIXED DEMENTIA

More than one type of dementia can occur simultaneously in the brain. In fact, recent studies suggest that mixed dementia is more common than previously thought. For example, the abnormal protein deposits associated with LBD can coexist with blood vessel problems linked to vascular dementia. Alzheimer's brain changes can also coexist with Lewy bodies. In some cases, a person may have brain changes linked to all three conditions — Alzheimer's disease, vascular dementia, and LBD.

CHAPTER TWO

The Importance of an Early Diagnosis

Although an early diagnosis is beneficial, about half of people with Alzheimer's and other dementias have not been diagnosed. LBD is the most misdiagnosed form of dementia, on average, taking more than 18 months and three doctors to receive a correct diagnosis.

EARLY SIGNS OF DEMENTIA

The early warning signs of dementia can be subtle and ambiguous. As a result, symptoms may not be immediately recognizable and go unnoticed at first. To make matters worse, those with dementia often do not recognize symptoms in themselves or are in a state of denial.

Early symptoms depend on the type of dementia and vary from person to person. In the previous chapter, I described some specific symptoms of different types of dementia. In general, however, you can look out for the following 10 common signs:

- memory loss
- increasing confusion especially regarding time and place
- difficulty performing normal daily tasks
- vocabulary problems
- difficulty concentrating
- disorientation

- apathy, fatigue, and withdrawal
- misplacing of things
- poor judgement and decision-making
- personality and behavior changes such as becoming suspicious, depressed, fearful, or anxious
- spatial and visual problems including an inability to judge distance or difficulty reading

If you notice any of the symptoms listed above, be sure and talk to your parent's doctor right away. Keep in mind, many people, especially the elderly, have memory loss or issues with motor skills. This does not necessarily mean they have Alzheimer's or another type of dementia.

Strokes, alcohol abuse, infections, thyroid disorders, depression, nutritional deficiencies, drug interactions, and brain tumors can all cause dementia-like symptoms. Many of these conditions can be treated.

GETTING AN ACCURATE DIAGNOSIS

Be forewarned. Even after you begin noticing some symptoms and see a physician, getting a correct diagnosis is difficult. Success often depends on your parent's doctor's knowledge and attitude about dementia.

When Mom was in her early 70s, she began having problems keeping appointments straight and sometimes forgot words, misplaced jewelry, or became lost driving to familiar places. She tended to downplay these problems and our family made the common mistake of chalking up these early symptoms to old age.

Nonetheless, I was a bit worried and described Mom's symptoms to her regular primary care doctor during a check-up. Her doctor didn't seem overly concerned nor did he suggest testing for dementia.

As time progressed, my mother's posture became hunched over and we took her to a specialist. After examining an x-ray, the doctor told us that she was in advanced stages of osteoarthritis and that the bones of her neck were collapsing into each other. Only later did we realize that this type of stooped posture is a symptom of LBD and Parkinson's. The specialist never suggested that this was even a remote possibility.

As my mother's concentration and memory began to worsen, our family became increasingly suspicious that Mom had some form of dementia. After she had hip replacement surgery, however, there was no longer any doubt.

After surgery, Mom didn't recognize me or other family members. She couldn't comprehend that she was in the hospital. Intense paranoid hallucinations and night terrors kept her awake in a state of panic all night. The hospital staff told us that these symptoms are not uncommon in the elderly after major surgery and that we shouldn't be overly concerned.

Later, I learned that people with LBD are particularly sensitive to general anesthesia and often display these types of symptoms after surgery. One of the many reasons an early diagnosis would have been beneficial to us.

Although my Mom's mind improved somewhat over time, mentally she was never the same again. Unfortunately, this is not a rare outcome for those with LBD who undergo major surgery with general anesthesia.

After we brought Mom home, her symptoms improved somewhat, but she still didn't always recognize me or other family members, night terrors continued, and pain medications made hallucinations much worse.

The nurses and physical therapists that visited her home during recovery told us, once again, that it wasn't unusual for the elderly to suffer from these kinds of symptoms after major surgery with general anesthesia. No one suggested that LBD could be the culprit.

Frustrated, I made an appointment with Mom's regular physician. This time, I was determined to find some answers.

TESTS FOR DEMENTIA

After emphasizing the severity of my mother's symptoms, her primary care physician performed several tests.

Although Alzheimer's and LBD can only be diagnosed with complete accuracy after death with a brain autopsy, experts estimate a skilled physician can diagnose different types of dementia with more than 90 percent accuracy.

Procedures vary, but typically an evaluation will include the following assessments:

- My mother's evaluation began by reviewing her medical history, current medications, and health issues. Since this is standard procedure, be prepared to fully describe any symptoms your parent is experiencing with memory problems, movement difficulties, sleep problems, as well as any behavior and mood changes. My Mom was embarrassed by her symptoms and tended to downplay them during doctor visits. If your parent tries to interfere, ask to speak with the doctor privately. Diagnosis is more accurate if the doctor has all the necessary information. Have a complete list of all current medications including prescriptions, over-the-counter-drugs, vitamins, and supplements.

- A physical examination is usually performed along with a neurological exam that includes testing reflexes, coordination, muscle strength, eye movement, and speech. Laboratory tests, such as blood and urine tests may be ordered and can help identify any illnesses, infections, or vitamin deficiencies that could be responsible for symptoms.
- Cognitive testing is often used to assess thinking abilities including memory, language, attention and problem-solving. In our case, these tests were revealing. The doctor asked my mother to remember three objects and then a few minutes later repeat the names. She was able to do so and I briefly felt relieved. But when the doctor asked my Mom what year it was, she clearly didn't know the answer and looked at me pleadingly for help. "Nineteen...." she began guessing. She couldn't draw a clock correctly either.
- Brain scans, such as a CT (computed tomography), MRI (magnetic resonance imaging), or PET (positron emission tomography) scan, may be ordered. I assumed my Mom's MRI would lead to a diagnosis, which was not the case. Many people are unaware of this fact, but now I know that no single test can determine if a person has Alzheimer's or LBD.

SEEING A SPECIALIST

"You knew something wasn't right, didn't you?" the doctor asked when we returned to discuss the results of my Mom's tests. By that time, we did; but the question seemed odd and insensitive.

In our case, Mom's primary doctor acknowledged that she had "some kind of dementia" but did not give us a specific diagnosis nor encourage us to seek a specialist to determine which type. Instead, he told us that there was no cure for dementia or treatments that change the course of the disease. Therefore, he informed us, the medical field could do little to help us.

Flabbergasted, I didn't want to accept his advice. Surely, something could be done to help us!

When we got home, I encouraged Mom to see a specialist, but she feared more testing which she hated and found humiliating. Besides, Alzheimer's sounded scary and embarrassing to her. Mom told me that if she had the disease, she preferred not to know.

After researching the different types of dementia on the Internet, I immediately saw that Mom had almost every symptom listed for LBD.

Unfortunately, I allowed my mother's feelings and her doctor's advice to prevent me from getting a formal diagnosis.

That was a mistake.

After a medication caused severe hallucinations, desperate for help, I took Mom to an urgent care facility. A doctor, whose own parent had suffered from dementia, asked to talk to me privately. She stressed the importance of seeing a specialist who had the experience and expertise to determine which specific type of dementia was causing my mother's symptoms.

Although dementia cannot be cured, she said, there are ways to help manage symptoms and having an accurate diagnosis would help us improve quality of life and plan for the future.

How right she was!

Depending on symptoms, a neurologist, geriatrician, or psychiatrist, may be recommended. In our case, a neurologist immediately recognized Mom's symptoms and after more testing, she was finally diagnosed with LBD.

BENEFITS OF GETTING AN EARLY DIAGNOSIS

The unknown is scary. Our family was comforted, in a way, to know what was causing my mother's bizarre behavior and what we could expect in the future. Although Mom had originally objected to being diagnosed, in the end, she was relieved to have a name for all the strange symptoms she was experiencing.

An early diagnosis can be valuable in other ways as well:

- A specialist can help you find the right treatment plan that can include medications and lifestyle changes to help with symptoms.
- Health advisers can answer your questions, help you understand the different progressive stages of the disease, and anticipate your parent's needs. They can also direct you to support services. Since dementia will progressively get worse, it's important to develop a relationship with doctors, health care professionals, and support services while you have the time to do so.

- Having a diagnosis can help you, as the caregiver, make better informed medical decisions. For example, as mentioned previously, people with LBD are often extremely sensitive to prescription and over-the-counter medications such as antihistamines, tranquilizers, sleep-aids, and pain medications. We had to find this out the hard way, which could have been prevented with a proper diagnosis. In addition, if my Mom had been diagnosed before her hip surgery, we could have discussed the risks and other possible alternatives to general anesthesia such as a spinal or regional block.
- A diagnosis will help you plan for the future and allow your parent to express his or her wishes regarding care and living options. In addition, your loved one can organize financial and legal affairs while still able to do so.

CHAPTER THREE

Exploring Treatments

After you receive a diagnosis, you'll need to work closely with doctors to create the best treatment plan for your parent. Make sure you fully understand all the available choices and the benefits as well as the side effects and risks of each option. Keep in mind, your treatment plan will probably change as the disease progresses and symptoms worsen.

DRUG TREATMENTS

Unfortunately, there aren't any drugs available today that will cure or slow the development of common types of dementia. Nonetheless, some medications may help temporarily lessen symptoms in some people.

The U.S. Food and Drug Administration (FDA) has approved two types of medications for Alzheimer's: cholinesterase inhibitors and memantine. These drugs may lessen and stabilize cognitive symptoms including memory loss, confusion, and problems with thinking and reasoning.

Namzaric combines both types of drugs in one medication for more convenient treatment.

According to the Alzheimer's Association, these drugs can temporarily slow worsening of symptoms for about half of those with Alzheimer's who take them for six to 12 months.

Although these drugs were developed to treat Alzheimer's, the Lewy Body Dementia Association (LBDA) states that "some researchers believe that people with

LBD may be even more responsive to these types of medications [cholinesterase inhibitors] than those with Alzheimer's."

Drug treatments are especially tricky for those with LBD. Antipsychotic medications can worsen parkinsonian symptoms such as rigid muscles, slow movement, and lack of balance. On the flip side, drugs typically used to reduce parkinsonian symptoms may increase confusion, hallucinations, and delusions.

Antipsychotic medications must be used with extreme caution regardless of the type of dementia. Recent research has shown that these drugs are associated with an increased risk of stroke and death in older adults with dementia.

Interestingly, "cholinesterase inhibitors have also been shown to be effective in treating hallucinations and other psychiatric symptoms of LBD," LBDA's site explains.

Antidepressants and anti-anxiety medications are sometimes used to treat depression, anxiety, and irritability which are common symptoms for dementia.

Make sure your physician and pharmacist are aware of all medications your parent is currently taking (including over-the-counter) to avoid any harmful interactions.

Whether your parent has Alzheimer's, LBD, or another type of dementia, the benefits from drugs are minimal and should be only one part of a person's overall care. Non-drug treatments such as lifestyle changes (see below) and other kinds of support are just as important.

LIFESTYLE CHANGES

As described in Chapter 2, in early stages, your parent may experience irritability, anxiety, and agitation. The lifestyle changes listed below can be helpful in addressing these behaviors.

- Create a calm and quiet environment. People suffering from dementia are typically sensitive to their surroundings. Clutter, noise, or poor lighting can all have an adverse effect.
- Speak in soft tones and avoid confrontation. People with dementia are unable to reason, so quarreling based on logic or even facts is simply not going to work.
- Make sure your parent is kept comfortable. Pain, hunger, thirst, illness, constipation, a full bladder, fatigue, infections, adverse reactions to medication, and skin irritations can all cause behavioral problems.

- Keep a regular routine. Any changes in caregiving arrangements, surroundings, or schedule can cause anxiety. Remember, your parent is trying to make sense out of an increasingly confusing world which can make any kind of adjustment unsettling.
- Make sure your loved one stays well rested between stimulating events. I quickly learned that scheduling two appointments on one day was too much for my Mom – and as her caregiver – for me too. Too many visitors at one time was distressing to her as well.

For more information, see Chapter 6 for tips on communicating with a person with dementia and Chapter 7 for advice on dealing with behavior issues.

VITAMINS, HERBS, AND OTHER SUPPLEMENTS

Many products are available on the market promising benefits. However, to date, there is no evidence that any kind of vitamins, herbs, or supplements can cure dementia or prevent, delay, or improve symptoms.

Since these alternative treatments may have an adverse effect or serious interactions with prescribed medication, always consult a physician before giving your parent any type of supplement.

ALTERNATIVE THERAPIES

Depending on the person, counselling, psychotherapy and cognitive behavioral therapy may be helpful. Therapy offers an opportunity to speak confidentially to a trained professional about upsetting symptoms, problems, or issues.

Physical and occupational therapy can be useful. In addition, a range of therapies outside of conventional medicine such as acupuncture, aromatherapy, music therapy, massage, and pet therapy may be effective in addressing some symptoms. Speak to a medical professional for advice and information before moving forward.

As time goes on, through trial and error, you'll find the best treatments and lifestyle changes that work for you and your loved one. Remember, what works today may not work tomorrow. Be observant and stay flexible.

CHAPTER FOUR

The Seven Stages of Dementia

All types of dementia are progressive. Learning about the different stages of dementia can guide you as a caregiver so you know what to expect. It can help you prepare emotionally, make plans for the future, determine the best approach to treatment, and improve communications with your parent's doctor.

Keep in mind, these stages vary widely according to the type of dementia and each person's experience with dementia is unique.

That means it's impossible to know exactly how a person's dementia will develop. The following is only meant to give you a general idea of how dementia typically progresses.

Try not to be overwhelmed by the list of symptoms during later stages. The progression is gradual, giving you time to adjust to the changes that occur. Tackle this disease one step at a time and don't dwell on the future.

STAGE 1: NORMAL

During this stage of no cognitive decline, your parent functions normally, has no memory loss, and is mentally healthy. In fact, stages 1-3 of dementia progression are generally known as "pre-dementia."

STAGE 2: AGE–ASSOCIATED SYMPTOMS

This stage of slight cognitive decline is associated with normal forgetfulness that often comes with aging.

For example, your parent may forget names or lose track of keys temporarily. Symptoms are barely noticeable and not obvious to you or your parent's doctor at this point.

STAGE 3: MILD DECLINE

You and others will probably start noticing the cognitive decline during this stage that often includes increased forgetfulness, a slight difficulty concentrating, and decreased work performance.

Your parent may get confused driving or have difficulty finding the right words. Planning and organizing skills begin to disintegrate. This stage can last seven years before the onset of dementia. Typically, a proper diagnosis is difficult to attain during this time.

STAGE 4: EARLY STAGE

Although your parent may still function independently, you may notice worsening symptoms that includes a struggle to concentrate and remember recent events, trouble managing finances, and withdrawal from family and friends as socialization becomes more difficult.

Personality and mood changes such as anxiety and depression may begin to take place as well. In a state of denial, your loved one may avoid challenging situations to hide symptoms that increasingly interfere with day-to-day life.

A doctor can usually detect cognitive problems during a patient interview and exam during this stage.

STAGE 5: MODERATE DEMENTIA

As the disease progresses, your parent will have major memory deficiencies and require a greater level of care. People in this stage often forget names of extended family members or their own home address and phone number. In a state of confusion, your loved one may become disoriented and not know the time or day.

STAGE 6: MODERATELY SEVERE DEMENTIA

Your loved one will need full-time care during this stage to carry out daily activities like preparing meals, bathing, and getting dressed. Delusions, hallucinations, compulsive behavior, agitation, wandering, urinary incontinence, sleep issues, anxiety, and aggression often begin during this time.

Your parent may forget the name of close family members such as a spouse or child or become unaware of surroundings. Even if you've been caring for your parent full-time to this point, you may want to enlist the help of professional caregivers and services.

STAGE 7: SEVERE DEMENTIA

In late-stage dementia, people eventually lose the ability to communicate and walk. Your parent will require round-the-clock assistance with most activities including eating and using the toilet. During this difficult stage you'll need help and support from family and friends as well as services such as hospice at the end of life.

SECTION TWO: CARING FOR A PARENT WITH DEMENTIA

CHAPTER FIVE

Caring for Your Parent's Physical Needs

Although most people associate dementia with memory loss, this disease will affect your parent in physical ways as well. Be prepared, your parent's health will noticeably decline as the dementia progresses requiring your assistance on many levels.

If you can help your loved one stay as healthy, mobile, and fit as possible, your parent will feel better and remain independent longer. As a result, it will be easier for you to care for your parent and the time you spend together will be more pleasant for both of you. In fact, there are many things you can do to make life more dignified and enjoyable during this time.

Keep in mind that as the dementia progresses, your loved one will lose the ability to identify health problems or explain symptoms. As a result, you'll need to keep a close eye on your parent's health and well-being.

Look out for warning signs or signals that your parent might be sick, in pain, or uncomfortable.

Be proactive. Don't wait for a crisis to make needed changes. If a strategy doesn't work, reassess the circumstances and with persistence and creativity, you can usually improve the situation.

The following are some suggestions, but keep in mind that every person with dementia has different physical needs and abilities as well as preferences.

PROVIDE A BALANCED DIET

Eating properly is important to keep your parent's body strong and healthy. Poor nutrition can worsen behavioral symptoms, cause weight loss, increase confusion, and contribute to bladder and bowel problems.

Provide a balanced diet with a variety of healthy foods including vegetables, fruits, whole grains, low-fat dairy products, and lean protein. That being said, making sure your loved one is eating enough nutritious foods isn't always easy.

In the early stages of dementia, your parent may develop a sweet tooth which can lead to weight gain. If that's the case, try offering low-calorie or healthy alternatives. For example, treats such as fat-free vanilla pudding with raspberries or juice-sweetened baked goods may help.

In later stages, the opposite problem develops. For example, my mother lost her appetite, complained food didn't taste right, and sometimes literally forgot to eat or drink. Even foods she loved in the past no longer appealed to her. As a result, weight loss became an issue.

When this happens, try the following:

- Make meals enjoyable in a calm environment. Turn off the TV and play soft music. If you sit down and eat with your parent, your loved one may mimic your actions. Invite other family members to eat with you when possible to make meals a happy occasion.
- Several small meals and nutritious snacks throughout the day can work better than three large meals.
- Supplement meals with high-protein/calorie drinks such as Ensure. My sister often made milkshakes with ice cream, fruit, and protein powder which Mom enjoyed.
- Keep choices simple. As the disease progresses, your parent may become confused when offered too many options at once.
- People with dementia, especially those suffering from LBD, often struggle with cutlery. Finger foods such as sandwiches, chicken drumsticks, hard boiled eggs, whole fruit, and vegetables are good options. Keep in mind, eating healthy foods and your parent's independence is more important than proper table manners.
- When chewing and swallowing becomes an issue, use soft foods and cut foods into small, bite-sized pieces. Foods can also be ground in a blender or baby food grinder if necessary.
- If your loved one refuses to eat a balanced diet, doctors may suggest alternatives or prescribe vitamins or supplements.

BEWARE OF DEHYDRATION

Watch carefully for dehydration. Warning signs include fatigue, dizziness, thirst, dark urine, headaches, dry mouth/nose, dry skin, increased confusion, and cramping.

Have water accessible always and offer clear fluids throughout the day. Sipping small amounts is usually easier than drinking large amounts all at once.

High water-content foods can also help replenish fluids. Fruits like watermelons, pears, pineapples, apples, strawberries, mangos, oranges, tomatoes, and grapes as well as vegetables such as salad greens, cucumbers, zucchini, or celery are good choices. Or try homemade popsicles made from fruit juice.

If your parent is having problems swallowing fluids or difficulty holding a glass, try a child's sippy cup or using straws. As my Mom's disease progressed, her head drooped severely, and she was unable to tilt her head back to drink. In fact, she was forced to constantly stare down at her feet. "I notice shoes now," she'd joke. God bless Mom. To make matters worse, her lower lip slacked. I learned to carry straws in my purse to make drinking in restaurants easier and less embarrassing.

HELP YOUR PARENT STAY ACTIVE

Staying physically active as long as possible will help your parent keep mobile, retain the ability to perform daily activities, and reduce the risk of falling by improving strength and balance. Other benefits include improved circulation, prevention of stiff muscles, healthier bones, and improved sleep quality. On top of all that, exercise is known to help mentally by reducing anxiety and depression, increasing self-esteem, and improving mood.

In early stages of dementia, your parent may still be able to play sports, do a bit of housework or gardening, walk, or participate in other physical activities. If that's the case, encourage your parent to continue these activities as long as possible. If your parent wasn't active before and resists the idea of exercising, try different kinds of beginner's workouts. Many are available on YouTube. Or encourage your parent to take a pleasant stroll around the block. Try to find something that your parent enjoys.

As the disease progresses and your parent has difficulty walking, chair-based exercises at home can be beneficial. Ask your doctor or occupational therapist for suggestions. If encouragement is needed, do the exercises with your parent and add some music to make it more fun.

Keep in mind that dementia patients should not exercise beyond their ability. If your parent experiences pain or feels unwell during any physical activity, stop immediately, and seek medical advice.

REDUCE THE RISK OF FALLING

One study found that those with Alzheimer's are three times more likely to suffer from hip fractures than those without the disease. Problems with vision, depth perception, a slow reaction time, and lack of balance increases the risk. The danger of falling is even greater for those with LBD because of the added Parkinsonian symptoms that include rigidity, loss of motor skills, and a shuffled walk. Although falls cannot always be prevented, here are a few tips to reduce the danger:

- Remove tripping hazards such as rugs and cords as well as clothes and shoes that may be left on the floor.
- Decrease clutter and make clear paths inside and outside the home.
- Improve lighting both inside and outside the home.
- Make sure your parent wears proper shoes with non-slip soles.
- Keep items that are used daily on lower shelves that can be easily reached.
- Use non-slip mats in the bathtub and on shower floors.
- Install grab bars next to the toilet and in the shower and bath.
- To help prevent wandering at night, keep important items, such as water, a light source, tissues, eye glasses, and a telephone on a bedside table.

An occupational therapist can provide information on aids and equipment that may help your loved one move around safely. A fall alert bracelet or necklace is extremely helpful, especially as the disease progresses.

If your parent falls, remain calm. Check for any injuries. If you are alone and your parent is too heavy to lift by yourself, call 911 for assistance.

LEARN PROPER TRANSFER TECHNIQUES

In early stages of dementia, when your parent may have trouble getting out of a chair but is still physically able to so, encourage your loved one to remain independent as long as possible. This will help your parent maintain muscle strength. A high, firm arm chair is easier to get out of than a deep sofa or overstuffed chair. A raised toilet seat is also helpful and can be easily purchased.

If you plan on buying a motorized lift chair, purchase it in the early stages of the disease so your parent can adjust to using the chair. We got a lift chair with simple controls for Mom, but the dementia had already progressed to the point she was unable to learn how to operate it properly.

Eventually, in later stages, you'll need to transfer your parent in and out of bed as well as on and off a chair, toilet, or wheelchair. At first, inexperienced with the task, I held Mom's hands and wrists and leaned back, using my body weight to lift her. This method frightened my mother who thought both of us might fall. Thankfully, that never happened.

However, later I learned that this technique is not only risky but may also cause muscle and joint strain or injury to the patient or the caregiver.

With that in mind, experts recommend the following steps:

If you're lifting your parent from a chair or toilet:
- Stand in front of your parent. Place your parent's feet, preferably with shoes or non-skid socks on, firmly on the floor. Make sure that your feet are shoulder-width apart and as close as possible to your parent's feet.
- Clasp your arms around your parent's waist or use a wide lifting belt fastened around your parent's waist for a secure grip.
- Ask your parent to lean forward and push off the chair to help you. If your parent is unable to do so, count to three and then lift. Use the muscles in your legs and not your back.
- As you lift, keep your knees bent and your back straight. Do not twist your body or allow your parent to pull on your neck.
- Give your loved one time to adjust to standing before moving since people with dementia react slowly.
- If your parent is too heavy for you to lift safely, get help.

If you're lifting your parent from bed, ask your loved one to push up to a sitting position. If your parent is unable to do so:
- Put one of your arms under your parent's legs and your other arm under the back.
- Move your parent's legs over the edge of the bed while rotating your loved one's body until your parent is sitting on the edge of the bed.
- Position your parent's feet on the floor slightly apart and then lift your loved one as instructed above.

If you're transferring your parent to a wheelchair:

- Place the chair close to the bed and lock the wheels before lifting your parent.
- Lift your parent as previously instructed, pivot toward the chair, bend your knees, and lower your parent into the chair. Make sure your parent's hands are on the arms of the chair before lowering.

Portable lifts can be used if your parent is too heavy to lift or has fallen. Be forewarned, a lift takes practice for both you and your parent before used safely.

Physical therapists and occupational therapists can provide valuable hands-on training and demonstrate transfer techniques, strengthening exercises, as well as recommend the right equipment for your situation. Some insurance policies will cover a home visit consultation with a doctor's referral.

LIMIT OR ELIMINATE ALCOHOL

Talk to your parent's doctor about whether alcohol should be allowed. Circumstances such as the severity of dementia, harmful interactions with medications, and the amount of alcohol being consumed need to be considered.

In early stages of dementia, Mom enjoyed having a glass of wine occasionally and we saw no need to take this pleasure away. However, some people with dementia drink too much and, as a result, become more confused or disoriented. Some forget how many drinks were consumed because of the disease and accidentally overindulge.

If you need to limit the amount of alcohol your parent consumes, keep alcohol out of sight, provide low alcohol or non-alcoholic substitutes, or water down drinks. If your parent drinks alcohol, be sure your loved one does not drive, wander off, or climb stairs while under the influence.

ASSIST WITH PERSONAL HYGIENE

Those with dementia often have difficulty with personal hygiene or simply forget or lose interest in such matters. Brushing or combing hair, bathing, shaving, clipping fingernails, and washing your parent's face will probably become an issue.

When this happens, offer reminders, keep daily routines consistent, and use simple instructions. An electric razor can make shaving easier and your parent may enjoy a manicure or pedicure from time to time.

As the disease progresses and your parent becomes immobile, your loved one will need assistance bathing. Keep the following tips in mind:

- Use safety features such as a transfer bench, non-slip floor mats, grab bars, a shower seat, a handled sponge, and a hand-held shower. Many people with dementia have depth perception problems so that stepping into a bathtub seems scary. If this is the case, consider converting your parent's tub so it has a door on the side.
- Don't leave a person with advanced dementia unattended in the bathtub or shower. Have soap, shampoo, a washcloth, and any other bath items you'll need, along with the clothes your parent will wear laid out beforehand.
- If possible, allow your parent to choose whether a tub bath, shower, or sponge bath is preferred, which bath products to use, and the time of day to bathe.
- Older people are typically more sensitive to heat and cold, so make sure the temperature of the bathroom and water are comfortable.
- Allow your loved one to do as much of the bathing as possible, giving step-by-step instructions if necessary. Doing so will help your parent retain a sense of independence, control, and accomplishment.
- When assistance is required, tell your parent what you are going to do ahead of time, explaining each step.
- Your parent's privacy and dignity are important. When it's necessary to assist your parent, wash one body part at a time and use a towel to cover the rest of the body. If at all possible, leave private areas for your parent to wash.
- If your parent refuses to bathe, try again later. If this becomes a recurring problem, try using distractions like chatting about a grandchild or soothing music to make bathing a pleasant experience.

MAKE DRESSING EASIER

People with dementia should be encouraged to dress on their own as long as possible. When your parent begins to struggle, becomes easily frustrated, or is in danger of falling while getting dressed, supervise and help as needed.

If possible, allow your parent the dignity of choosing what to wear. Don't worry if the clothes don't match. Offer two or three options at a time since too many choices can be confusing. If your parent insists on wearing a favorite outfit day after day, buy duplicates or triplicates.

Arrange the clothes in the order they should be put on to reduce any confusion. If needed, hand your parent one item at a time or give clear, step-by-step instructions. Provide a suitable chair with arms if your parent has poor balance.

As the disease progresses and you must dress your parent, do so with tact and sensitivity. Allow plenty of time so that neither of you feels rushed or stressed. Change one piece of clothing at a time, keeping as much of your parent's body covered as possible to give your loved one privacy.

Loose-fitting, comfortable clothes with elastic waistbands, easy zippers, or snaps, and clothes that fasten in the front will make life easier. Avoid buttons. Buy shoes that are comfortable and easy to put on, preferably with Velcro. Remove clothing from the closet that is too frustrating to put on or take off.

KEEP TEETH AND GUMS HEALTHY

Ensuring your parent's teeth are brushed and gums are kept healthy is important. Poor dental hygiene can lead to heart disease, gingivitis, stroke, osteoporosis and respiratory disease. In addition, infections can worsen the confusion associated with dementia and any pain or discomfort may lead to difficulties with eating and drinking.

In early stages, a simple reminder may do the trick. As your parent's dementia progresses, supervision or assistance is often required. Eventually, you'll probably need to take over brushing your parent's teeth with a more hands-on approach. This is usually easier if your parent sits in a chair and you brush teeth from behind. When flossing your parent's teeth, a floss holder can be helpful.

Remember, sitting quietly while someone sticks objects and works inside your mouth can be unpleasant and even frightening to someone with dementia. So, use a soft voice and patiently explain the steps you will take before proceeding.

Be flexible and find a time when both of you are calm and have time to devote to the task. Teeth don't have to be brushed early in the morning or late at night.

If your parent wears dentures and is no longer capable of caring for them, you'll need to remove the dentures daily to clean and check gums for any irritation.

Regular dental check-ups are essential. Find a dentist who understands dementia who will work patiently with you and your parent. Keep an eye out for frequent pulling, rubbing, or touching of the face or mouth, moaning, increased restlessness, or disturbed sleep which could indicate dental problems.

MANAGE INCONTINENCE

One of the most difficult and distressing symptoms of dementia, both for the caregiver and your loved one, is the eventual incontinence that occurs.

If your parent forgets to use the toilet, remind your loved one on a regular basis – every two to three hours – to reduce accidents. Discreetly watch for warning signs that your parent may have to go to the bathroom such as fidgeting, pacing, restlessness, or pulling at clothes.

Incontinence pads will eventually become a necessity and can be purchased at any grocery or drug store. Use a mattress protector and easy-to-remove clothing that is easily washable. Pay attention to your parent's skin as urine and feces can irritate and cause rashes.

Limit fluids before bedtime to help prevent accidents at night. Be sure your parent has a night light or motion sensor. In some cases, a urinal bottle or commode next to the bed at night is useful.

Most dementia patients are mortified by incontinence problems. Try to allow your parent to keep their dignity intact as much as possible. When there is an accident, stay calm and reassuring. Distract your loved one and clean up quietly and discreetly.

CONSTIPATION

Constipation is common with old age. Dementia can make the problem worse since your parent will become less active and forget to use the bathroom regularly as the disease progresses.

With that in mind, be aware of the time of day when your parent normally has a bowel movement, so you can provide a gentle reminder if necessary.

While your parent doesn't need to have a bowel movement every single day, as a rule, experts say that three days without defecation is cause for concern. Keep in mind that your loved one may not understand or be able to articulate the discomfort from constipation.

Try increasing fluid and fiber in your parent's diet and encouraging more physical activity. A small glass of prune juice can do wonders. If this fails to do the trick, ask your doctor about the possibility of giving psyllium preparations (such as Metamucil or Citrucel). If you suspect bowel impaction, consult a doctor immediately.

WATCH CAREFULLY FOR BEDSORES

Anyone caring for a person with dementia should be aware of the serious risk of bedsores, sometimes called pressure ulcers.

Bedsores can develop extremely quickly, especially during late stages of the disease when your parent becomes immobile. Those with dementia are at additional risk because of communication difficulties that may prevent them from letting caregivers know if they are in pain or need to move. If early signs are not noticed or ignored, these sores can become painful, infected, and even life-threatening.

If your parent is in a nursing home or rehabilitation facility, do not take for granted that your loved one is out of danger. In fact, the highest percentage of people with bedsores are in nursing homes.

This is a subject close to my heart. Tragically, bedsores developed on my Mom's lower back while in a rehabilitation center after fracturing her hip. The sores were not detected by the staff, began tunneling, and became infected. Antibiotics were ineffective. There is no doubt in my mind, these excruciatingly painful pressure ulcers contributed to her death.

Experts recommend taking the following steps to prevent this calamity from happening:

- Encourage your parent to get up during the day and move around as much as possible, either independently or with your help. Use an alarm if necessary to help you both remember.
- Check your loved one's skin when you help your parent bathe or dress, especially around bony areas. Bed sores are most likely to appear on the heels, ankles, knees, buttocks, hips, spine, tailbone, elbows, shoulder blades and the back of the head.
- If you see any red patches or even a small red dot, this may well be an early sign of pressure ulcers. Do NOT ignore these signs and contact your parent's doctor immediately.
- If your parent is in a nursing home or rehabilitation center, make sure the staff is taking precautions to prevent and detect bedsores.

CHAPTER SIX

Communicating with Your Parent

Conversations with a person who has dementia can be challenging, complicated, and frustrating, especially as the disease progresses. You'll need a lot of patience and understanding as well as some strategies to communicate with your parent successfully.

At first, my mother had problems organizing her thoughts and finding the right word. This was more annoying to her than me.

As the disease progressed, however, she lost the ability to reason or to communicate logically. Her confusion and frustration caused her to become argumentative, unreasonable, irritable, angry, and critical. In later stages, Mom became delusional, paranoid, and accusatory.

Be prepared, this is a common scenario. Before you throw up your hands in defeat, however, try some of the suggestions I've listed below. Keep in mind, some days will be better than others. Caregivers can't always be perfect – I certainly wasn't – but if you strive to put these tips to use, life will be easier.

BEGIN A DISCUSSION RIGHT

Establish a positive atmosphere before you begin talking by keeping the following strategies in mind:

- Sit down so you are at eye level with your parent. Hovering over your parent may feel intimidating or condescending.
- Make sure your body language is open, calm, and relaxed.

- Reduce the noise level and distractions. Ensure you have your parent's attention.
- Choose the right time to have serious discussions. Don't try to talk right before you have to leave or when your parent is in pain, sleepy, irritable, or hungry. Instead, choose a "good" day when your parent is calm, comfortable, and more alert.

BE AN EMPATHETIC LISTENER

Don't forget, your parent is losing independence, freedom, and capabilities. Be sympathetic. Listen carefully and try to respond to your parent's requests and questions – even if they are irrational – in a calm and respectful manner.

Acknowledge and validate your parent's feelings. When your parent feels anxious or frightened and lashes out, listen compassionately. Be generous with reassuring and comforting words. Tell your parent you understand, then provide assurance that everything is under control.

AVOID ARGUING AT ALL COSTS

Debating with your loved one trying to use reason, facts, or logic is pointless and only leads to more frustration for both of you. Take my word on this.

This part is hard, but even when your parent becomes unreasonable and argumentative, don't raise your voice. Make sure your body language and facial expressions do not show anxiety, anger, or impatience. Keep in mind that people with dementia are greatly influenced by the atmosphere and emotions of others.

Once again, this isn't easy, but try not to take negative comments, resentful remarks, or criticisms personally or fight back to defend yourself. Caregivers are only human, and you'll probably have a knee jerk reaction. Nonetheless, try to focus on the emotions your parent is experiencing, such as confusion or anxiety, in a compassionate way before responding. This takes self-control and practice, but the effort is worthwhile.

Finally, don't bother correcting your parent's every inaccurate statement which can start futile arguments. For example, one of my Mom's frequent hallucinations was of a cat sitting on her feet. At first, I tried to argue that there was no cat which only made her angry. After all, the "cat" was real to her. Eventually, I just pretended to remove the cat from the room which usually calmed her down.

So, if your loved one thinks the year is 1964 or a dead one is still alive, no harm done. Instead of quarreling about it, try to divert your parent's attention elsewhere.

KEEP CONVERSATIONS SIMPLE

Keep in mind that those with dementia cannot process too much information at once or juggle different threads of a conversation in their mind. Try the following:
- Stick to one subject at a time using familiar words.
- State your message slowly with plenty of pauses to allow your parent time to process the information.
- Patiently repeat statements if necessary.
- Avoid asking complicated questions that require thinking or memory skills.
- If your parent is struggling for an answer, gently suggest words.
- Break down tasks into easy step-by-step instructions.
- Don't offer too many choices at once which can be confusing.

TREAT YOUR PARENT AS AN ADULT

Resist the temptation to treat your parent like a child. This includes lecturing, baby talking, making demands, or talking to others as if your parent is not in the room.

Be respectful when making a request. Avoid the word "don't" if possible. For example, instead of saying, "Don't walk without your walker," hand your parent the walker and ask if your loved one needs help. Or rather than demanding, "Don't go outside," say, "Let's get a snack in the kitchen."

If you must overrule a parent's wishes, do so with kindness, open communication, and honest explanations.

DON'T LOSE YOUR SENSE OF HUMOR

Dementia is a horrific disease but, even on the worst days, funny and bizarre moments happen. If possible, laugh with your parent. Don't feel guilty. You're not laughing at your parent but at the ridiculous situations that randomly occur. Chances are that your parent will laugh harder than you.

Laughter relieved the pressure and saved my Mom and I from going crazy on many occasions. Your laughter during a challenging time when there are misunderstandings can lighten the moment and send a positive, comforting message to your parent.

WHEN COMMUNICATIONS GET OUT OF CONTROL

As the dementia progresses and your parent becomes more argumentative, communications may become volatile.

If your parent has an outburst, step back, take a deep breath, and regain your composure.

Acknowledge your parent's feelings and then try to redirect your loved one's attention.

Perhaps a change of scenery will help. You might say: "I'm sorry you're feeling so frustrated. Why don't we get something to eat at your favorite restaurant?"

If all else fails, try using physical touch to comfort and calm your parent. Sometimes simply holding your parent's hands or a gentle hug with a soothing voice and comforting smile will show you care and help your parent respond to you in a more positive manner.

Know your limitations.

If you feel unable to calmly communicate with your parent, perhaps a family member or friend can give you a break to recharge.

If this happens on a regular basis and you're unable to control your emotions while communicating and caring for your parent, you may want to consider other caregiving options (see Chapter 9).

CHAPTER SEVEN

Dealing with Behavior Issues

Caregiving for a person with dementia presents extra challenges such as wandering, paranoia, embarrassing conduct, and aggression. How to deal with these problems in an effective way can be baffling and distressing. You'll find that changing your reaction or taking preventative measures is often easier than trying to change your parent's behavior. Employing the strategies listed below can help you get through these trying times.

WANDERING

One day, Mom was watching the *Rachel Ray Show* at home and apparently fell asleep. She awoke confused, phoned my brother, and informed him that she was at Rachel's house and was going to walk "home." Although he tried to explain that she was already home, Mom wouldn't listen. Fortunately, she had trouble with the locks and our family arrived at Mom's house in time to stop her.

This was a wake-up call. With a pit in my stomach, I realized my formerly part-time job caring for my Mom had suddenly become a round-the-clock commitment. My husband and I sold our home and moved in with her.

However, it quickly became apparent that I couldn't watch Mom every second of the day and night. What was I supposed to do?

Wandering is a common problem for those with dementia. In fact, six in 10 people with dementia will wander, get lost, forget their name and address, and become disoriented, even in familiar places. If this happens, experts recommend the following precautions and strategies to help:

- Install new locks on the doors that require a key or add child-safe plastic covers to doorknobs.
- Motion detectors will alert you if your loved one opens the door.
- Keep car keys out of sight.
- Provide your parent with ID jewelry.
- Purchase a digital device that can be worn like a watch or clipped on that utilizes global positioning systems (GPS) or other technology that tracks the location of your parent.
- Be sure your neighbors are aware of your circumstances, so they can alert you if they see your parent wandering alone in the neighborhood. Give them your cell phone number.

Be aware that it is common for people with dementia to beg to go "home" while in their own house like my mother. When this first started happening, I pointed out family portraits and cherished items to my Mom, hoping she would recognize familiar things and realize she was already home. To no avail. Mom didn't believe me and became even more frantic.

If you try to correct your parent when this happens, most likely, your loved one won't believe you either and, if physically able, may wander off in search of "home" once you're out of sight. Instead, try explaining that you'll both be staying "here" a bit longer and will go home tomorrow. Hopefully, this will calm your parent and the entire episode will be forgotten by the next day.

DEPRESSION

A certain amount of depression is very common in people with dementia - particularly in the early stages when they may be aware of their declining abilities. You can help in the following ways:

- If your loved one is still mobile, regular physical exercise can help.
- Make a list of favorite restaurants, friends, gardens, museums, and other places your parent enjoys and try to visit often.
- Be sure that a loved one's normal activities, social events, and hobbies continue as long as possible.
- Spend time outdoors.
- If your parent is spiritual, nurture your loved one with soothing, inspirational activities.

- Allow your parent to talk about why they feel depressed. Listen attentively and show empathy.
- In the early stages, a support group where your parent can talk to others in a similar situation may be helpful. Individual counseling can work for those who aren't comfortable in a group setting.
- Offer lots of affection, reassurance, comfort, and support.
- Find ways that the person can contribute to family life and be sure to praise your parent's efforts. Show appreciation for all that your loved one has done for the family in the past as well.
- Celebrate any small accomplishments or successes.

ANXIETY AND AGITATION

Those with dementia often feel uneasy, upset, restless, and anxious. As a result, your parent may pace, fidget, or have trouble winding down to sleep.

If this is the case, the following suggestions may help:

- Ensure that the agitation is not caused by any kind of physical discomfort. Make sure your parent is not in pain, uncomfortable, hungry, or thirsty.
- As pointed out in Chapter 3, people suffering from dementia are typically sensitive to their surroundings, so create a calm, uncluttered, and quiet environment. Try not to make too many changes at once and keep a regular routine. Make sure your parent stays well rested.
- Since raising your voice or showing impatience will only worsen the situation, be sure and stay calm and speak in soft tones. Using effective methods of communication as listed in the previous chapter may help.
- Exercise can ease stress. If your parent is still able to do so, take an evening stroll together or do a little gardening.
- Provide lots of reassurance if the anxiety stems from fear, hallucinations, or paranoia. People with dementia may need to be reminded often that they are safe and everything is under control.
- Watch for early signs of agitation and then try to find ways to prevent the situation from getting worse. Sometimes crafts, soft music, a favorite movie, or another calm activity can divert your parent's attention.

SLEEP ISSUES

People with dementia often experience sleep disturbances and restlessness. Disorders like REM sleep behavior disorder, sleep apnea, and restless leg syndrome are common, worsening the situation.

Many become restless or agitated in the late afternoon or early evening, an experience referred to as "sundowning," which can continue late into the night.

Excessive daytime sleepiness is another frequent problem. For example, my Mom became prone to taking long naps. She would fall into such a deep slumber that she often awoke disoriented and unable to distinguish dreams from reality. These types of naps made her less likely to sleep through the night.

This is not unusual. Experts estimate that in late stages of dementia, individuals spend about 40 percent of their time in bed at night awake and a significant part of the day sleeping.

All these sleep disturbances can prevent both you and your parent from getting much-needed sleep.

The following strategies may help:

- Have a daily routine. Try to keep your loved one active and outside in the bright light for at least an hour a day to help improve sleep quality. Have a consistent time for going to bed and waking up in the morning.
- Avoid stimulants like nicotine, alcohol, chocolate, and caffeine in the late afternoon and evening. Have a large meal at lunch and a smaller meal at dinner.
- Don't plan any visits, activities, or appointments late in the afternoon. Instead, make outings earlier in the day so you can both return home with plenty of time to wind down and relax before bedtime.
- Keep evenings as simple, calm, and relaxing as possible. You might play soothing music or nature sounds, read something inspirational, or take a stroll. If your parent enjoys watching TV at night, try to avoid watching violent or action-packed movies or TV shows just before bedtime. Even the nightly news can be too stressful. Try light-hearted comedies, nostalgic movies, or family shows instead. My Mom loved to watch *Everybody Loves Raymond* or *Full House* reruns before going to sleep.
- This can be challenging but try not to allow your parent to nap excessively in daytime hours. In early stages of the disease, you can often keep your parent engaged and active with exercise, outings, or even simple chores during the day. If your loved one absolutely needs to sleep, try to limit naps to 20 to 30 minutes which should be adequate to provide rest without interfering with sleep at night.

- Keep your loved one's bedroom at a comfortable temperature.

If, despite all your efforts, your parent still keeps you up at night, perhaps a family member or friend can spend the night occasionally, so you can get some necessary shut-eye. My siblings did this for me and it made a big difference. If the problem becomes severe and you're unable to get any sleep on a nightly basis, consider hiring in-home caregivers to help at night.

While sleep medications are available, these drugs are usually used as a last resort, if at all. Side-effects in people with dementia include confusion, an increased risk of falling and fractures, dizziness, incontinence, and increased agitation.

REPETITIVE SPEECH AND ACTIONS

Those with dementia often ask the same questions, say the same things, or repeat actions like opening and closing a door.

Although this behavior can be exasperating for caregivers, usually it's harmless. Keep in mind that your parent is not doing this to purposely annoy you.

Your loved is unable to retain information. Therefore, your parent doesn't remember that he or she already said or did something. Nor will your parent recall that you already answered the same question several times.

Although saying, "I've told you the answer 20 times," or "You already told me that two seconds ago," is tempting, it will only make matters worse.

Try to listen patiently and answer questions calmly each time. Perhaps your loved one is repeating a question or statement to make sense of a situation, express a concern or fear, or receive reassurance. Or your parent may feel misunderstood or misinterpreted and is simply trying to get a message across.

Sometimes a repetitive behavior is triggered by frustration, anxiety, or boredom.

If this is the case, give your loved one a chore with meaningful purpose like sorting laundry or polishing silver. Or try a soothing activity like looking at a family photo album.

Look for possible ways of preventing this behavior. Depending on your parent and the stage of dementia, it may help to write down repeated questions and have the answers to these questions on post-it notes around the house or a chalkboard kept for this purpose.

Or if your parent keeps asking the time repeatedly, buy a large clock that is easy-to-read and keep it nearby in a visible place.

Perhaps this behavior occurs around certain people, activities, or surroundings or always takes place at a specific time of day. Look for a reason behind the repetition and you may be able to eliminate triggers.

Avoid discussing future appointments too far in advance. If I did so, my Mom would ask repeatedly when the event was taking place – literally for days – which drove me nuts. I quickly learned to never mention any planned appointments or outings until it was time to get ready.

If repetitive speech or an action is getting on your nerves, leave the room and take a deep breath. Get some fresh air or call a friend and vent. When you return, hopefully you'll be in better shape to deal with your parent's behavior.

DELUSIONS

Those with dementia often become suspicious and paranoid, falsely believing that others are plotting against them, following them, or trying to harm them. These delusions can take a variety of forms.

For example, your father may incorrectly believe that your mother is cheating on him. Or that your brother is an imposter. Or that the neighbor is plotting to take over his property.

If your parent is having delusions, don't bother trying to convince your loved one that the paranoid misbeliefs are untrue. It's futile.

After her hip replacement surgery, Mom became convinced that nurses were conspiring against us and doctors were planning to kidnap her. I couldn't persuade her otherwise.

Another time, Mom thought my sister had locked her in a non-existent cabin and was trying to do so again. When I tried to explain that wasn't the case, she looked at me suspiciously and whispered in a spooky tone, "You're in on it."

Paranoia often springs from confusion and fear. Instead of trying to convince your parent the delusions aren't real, listen patiently, acknowledge your loved one's feelings, and offer plenty of comfort and reassurance. Keep any necessary explanations short and simple. Then, try to distract your parent with a soothing activity.

If a delusion isn't driven by paranoia or fear, you may just want to ignore it. As Carol Bradley Bursack wrote in an article for AgingCare.com, "What did it hurt that [my father] thought he was helping plan the new zoo in Fargo, including finding an elephant for one of their exhibits? It kept him busy and helped him feel useful."

Of course, this is your personal choice, but I found that telling my mother she was wrong all the time didn't make her feel better. Instead, it often led to arguments and hurt feelings.

Another common delusion is the belief that people are stealing valuable belongings. Mom frequently accused the housekeepers of stealing her jewelry. I was always present while they were cleaning, and the same maids had been coming to her home for years without any trouble. If I reminded her of this fact or mentioned that she often forgot where she hid valuable jewelry, Mom became angry.

Of course, you should investigate any accusations that could possibly be true. However, if your parent is falsely accusing people of stealing things, try to learn where your loved one hides valuables, so you can prove this isn't the case. If possible, keep duplicates of the item. Explain to workers in the home and family members that paranoid accusations are part of dementia and are not meant to be taken personally. Likewise, if you're falsely accused, don't take offence.

If you are unable to locate the "missing item," try to gently change the subject and distract your parent. You could suggest: "Before we start looking for your bracelet, why don't we eat some lunch, then we'll look for it?" If you're lucky, by the time you finish the meal, your parent will forget all about it.

HALLUCINATIONS

While delusions are a false but strong belief in something that isn't real, hallucinations are slightly different. Hallucinations are sensory so that your parent sees, hears, smells, or feels something that isn't there.

Once again, trying to argue that your parent's hallucinations aren't real won't work. Although not grounded in reality, the situation is very real to your loved one.

If a hallucination doesn't cause your parent to feel threatened, afraid, or upset, you may not need to do or say anything. For example, my mother sometimes saw non-existent children playing in the backyard and laughed at their antics. No harm in that, so I left her alone.

On the other hand, if the hallucination is frightening your parent, act calmly and quickly.

Acknowledge your parent's feelings. For example, you might say, "I know this is scary for you." Then provide lots of reassurance that you will provide protection and keep your parent safe.

A gentle and comforting touch may turn your loved one's attention toward you and away from the hallucination.

If that doesn't work, the Alzheimer's Association suggests moving to another room, outside on the patio, or taking a walk to see if the hallucination recedes.

Or try to turn your parent's attention to music, conversation, or activities you enjoy together.

If a hallucination leads to aggression or the possibility of self-harm, seek professional help immediately.

INAPPROPRIATE BEHAVIOR

People with some forms of dementia may no longer recognize what is socially or sexually appropriate and lose their inhibitions.

This type of behavior is seen in a relatively small percentage of dementia cases, most commonly in men.

For example, your parent may make rude or sexual remarks, use foul language, masturbate, or begin undressing in front of guests. Although this type of speech or conduct is embarrassing and distressing, try to remain calm. Your parent probably doesn't even realize the behavior is wrong.

If your parent displays inappropriate behavior, calmly remove your parent from the situation and try to distract your loved one with another activity.

In some cases, taking steps to prevent these occurrences, such as modifying clothing to prevent easy removal or changing the sex of the caregiver when bathing or dressing, may help.

AGGRESSION

Aggressive behavior can occur during late-stages of dementia. Your parent may become hostile verbally by screaming, yelling, making threats, or swearing. Or your loved one may become physically aggressive by throwing objects, slapping, pinching, pulling hair, or scratching.

Although aggression can occur with no apparent reason at times, often this behavior is caused by physical discomfort, environmental factors, frustrations, medical conditions such as a urinary tract infection, or poor communication. In other words, your parent is most likely trying to communicate a need, not attacking you personally.

The Alzheimer's and Dementia Caregiver Center suggests that caregivers try to determine the cause behind the behavior as a first step. See your parent's doctor to rule out any medical causes. If your parent is tired, hungry, or uncomfortable, take care of any immediate needs. Perhaps your loved one is exasperated trying to communicate. If so, listen patiently and try to remain calm. Help with a frustrating task if needed. If too many visitors have become overwhelming, the TV is blaring too loud, or your parent's routine was disrupted, make any necessary changes or adjustments. Note any triggers so you can try to prevent the behavior in the future.

Experts say, regardless of the cause of an outburst, don't panic, resort to physical force, shout, or show fear or anxiety. This type of response will only increase your parent's agitation. Instead, from a safe distance encourage communication, listen carefully, and show you want to help with reassuring words. Perhaps music, massage or exercise will help pacify your parent.

If your parent continues to act aggressive despite your efforts, take a deep breath and step back to give your parent space and time to calm down. You may need to leave the room after making sure your parent is in a safe environment, then come back later and try again.

Of course, never put yourself in danger. If you feel threatened and your parent is unable to calm down, call 911 in emergency situations. Let the responders know your parent has dementia.

SECTION THREE: CARING FOR YOURSELF

CHAPTER EIGHT

Coping as a Caregiver

Caring for someone with dementia can easily become all-consuming and cause you to ignore your own needs. Don't make this mistake. You MUST take care of yourself during this tough time.

Experts often use the following illustration: On a plane, the flight attendant instructs parents to put on their own oxygen masks before putting masks on their children. As nurturers, this advice goes against all their instincts. But if they don't put on their mask first, they will become unconscious and unable to help their children.

The same principle applies to caregiving. The truth is that you won't be able to care for your loved one unless you care for yourself first.

If you don't keep yourself healthy – physically, spiritually, mentally, and emotionally – you'll become susceptible to sickness, burnout, and psychological problems, all of which can make it impossible to care for your parent.

Don't allow this horrible disease to claim two victims.

Of course, coping as a caregiver is easier said than done. Let's discuss some important things you can do to take care of your own personal needs.

CARE FOR YOURSELF PHYSICALLY

Caregiving for a parent with dementia is physically demanding and exhausting. To help retain your strength, be sure and follow the suggestions below:

- Fuel your body with a well-balanced diet. Do not skip meals. Healthy food choices supply your body with vitamins, minerals, and nutrients that keep you energized and strong. Don't forget to stay hydrated as well.
- Exercise not only keeps you stronger physically but also reduces stress. Try to get at least 30 minutes of exercise on most days of the week. If that amount of time seems impossible, break it up into 10-minute segments three times a day. Remember, a little exercise is better than none.
- Establish a good sleep routine. As discussed in the previous chapter, if your loved one is keeping you awake, have a family member or friend stay overnight occasionally to allow you to sleep.
- If you must help your parent move around or lift your loved one from chairs and/or a bed, be careful not to injure your back. See Chapter 5 for transferring tips.
- See a doctor for regular checkups. Keep an eye out for health problems worsened by stress such as high blood pressure or ulcers.

ACCEPT AND ASK FOR HELP

At first, you may be able to care for your parent alone. However, as the disease progresses, it's unlikely that you'll be equipped to care for another person 24 hours a day, seven days a week.

"It is absolutely essential," states *The 36-Hour Day*, "that you have regular times to 'get away' from twenty-four-hour care of the chronically ill person. You must have some time to rest and be able to do some things just for yourself...Taking time off, away from the care of [your parent], is one of the single most important things that you can do to make it possible for you to continue to care for someone."

That's good advice. Don't be afraid to ask for assistance so you can get a much-needed break. A little time apart is usually good for both you and your parent. The break could be an hour or two or a long weekend. Even a short amount of time can make a big difference.

Make a weekly schedule with family members if they live nearby so you can get relief on a regular basis. For instance, my youngest sister spent one day a week with our mother, my brother was available in the evenings and during weekends, my other sister helped when I had appointments or errands, and my husband and children pitched in as needed.

While family dynamics may be complicated and dealing with dementia is stressful, this is a time when the entire family needs to pull together.

Accept help when it's offered by friends, workmates, or members of your church. When people ask you to let them know how they can help, tell them. Be specific. Don't feel guilty. Of course, everyone has busy lives, but there are many simple tasks that aren't too burdensome. Maybe they can stay with your parent while you run an errand, bring by a meal, or do a bit of shopping. If you're too embarrassed to ask for help, make a list of some small chores and allow a friend or family member to delegate.

Adult day centers, in the early stages of dementia, can give you a break while providing activities in a safe environment. Your parent may be resistant to the idea at first, but if given time to adjust to the experience may enjoy socializing and joining in activities. Many centers offer services on sliding scales that allow caregivers to pay according to ability or income. In some states, Medicaid covers the cost for people with a very low income and few assets.

Local organizations and charities also provide "respite care." Find out what's available in your area.

TAKE TIME TO RELAX

When you do get a break from caregiving, be selfish. Don't spend the entire time running errands. Do something soothing that is purely for you. Go shopping for new shoes, enjoy a long bath with scented candles, get a massage, meet a friend for lunch, putter around in the garden, or splurge on a pedicure.

Remember, if your nerves are frayed because you never take time to unwind, you won't be able to deal with all the behavioral problems that accompany this disease in an appropriate way. Nurturing your own spirit by recharging will give you the strength and endurance to continue.

When one of my family members gave me a short hour break, I often headed for a nearby park, sat under a tree, listened to the birds sing, soaked up the sun, and read a book. It felt delightfully luxurious.

Creative activities can also reduce stress and help you relax. If you and your parent enjoy the same kind of activities – whether it's painting, writing, or crafts – depending on the stage of the disease, you may be able to share the experience together. If this is impossible, carve out some time for yourself to engage in your favorite hobby. Remember, you have the right to a life of your own outside of caregiving.

EMBRACE YOUR SPIRITUALITY

Faith consoles and comforts, offers a sense of purpose and fulfillment, and promises a better future. Do not neglect your spiritual side during this stressful time. If you're a religious person, now is the time to rely on your faith for strength.

Honestly, I wouldn't have been able to endure without prayer, meditation, and support from members of my congregation. Fortunately, my Mom and I shared the same faith. When we were unable to attend religious meetings, a phone hook-up was available so we both could listen and be strengthened and encouraged.

ACCEPT YOUR EMOTIONS

As I discussed in the introduction of this book, caregiving is a rollercoaster ride of emotions. If you've taken on the role as your parent's caregiver, it can be easy to set unrealistic expectations for yourself. No one is perfect and at times emotions can overwhelm even the most responsible caregiver.

Your feelings may include stress, depression, frustration, grief, helplessness, anxiety, guilt, irritability, restlessness, resentment, fear, and anger. Do not try and suppress these feelings. You have the right to feel any or all these emotions. Accept your feelings as a natural response to caregiving. You are only human.

Don't go through this process alone. Find someone in your life who you feel free to share all your conflicting emotions and troubling thoughts. Choose a trusted close friend, family member, or spiritual advisor who will listen, empathize, and encourage you. Talk to this person about your fears, frustrations, and doubts.

When you identify and accept your feelings, you can find productive ways to express and deal with those emotions. If you feel unable to do so, consider speaking to a professional therapist.

STAY CONNECTED

Often, caregivers feel socially isolated and disconnected from the outside world. Maintaining supportive relationships is important for your well-being.

If possible, arrange for time each week to catch up with your friends. Go to lunch, take a walk, or watch a movie together. If that's impossible, phone, email, or get in touch through social media.

Talking to other caregivers of loved ones with dementia in support groups may also help. Not only can you share your feelings and needs with others who will understand, but you can also exchange practical solutions and information and learn about resources available in your community. If you prefer, many online support groups are available.

FOCUS ON THE POSITIVE

When you're feeling overwhelmed or resentful, remind yourself why you made the choice to provide caregiving for your loved one.

While it's hard to focus on the positives of caregiving when there are so many challenges, having an optimistic attitude can help you get through the trying times.

Remember that caregiving is a meaningful, worthwhile, and important undertaking. During a time when your parent needs love and reassurance desperately, you're helping make your loved one feel secure, valued, and cherished.

If you're having a hard time seeing the positive achievements, write them down. When you are having a challenging day, this list can help you remember all the good you are accomplishing.

KNOW YOUR LIMITS

Many caregivers are juggling other responsibilities, such as demanding jobs and caring for their own families. If the stress of caregiving is left unchecked, it can take a toll on your health, relationships, and state of mind—eventually leading to burnout.

The fact is that about 60% of caregivers show signs of clinical depression and tend to take more prescription medication for anxiety and depression than other people in their age group.

Monitor yourself for symptoms of burnout. Signs can include anger, anxiety, irritability, depression, social withdrawal, exhaustion, and sleep problems.

If you've reached a crisis point, seek support from a mental health professional experienced in caregiver burnout and grief. Many clinics offer free or low-cost help.

If you're at the end of your rope and no longer able to provide full-time caregiving, be honest with yourself and investigate other options. Do not lose your sanity, marriage, and physical health for the sake of caregiving.

Shortly before my mother's death, our family hired full-time in-home caregivers. By this time, I was showing serious signs of burnout and should have gotten help sooner. Do not wait too long.

Even if you've managed for months or years to care for your parent, in late stages of dementia often your loved one's needs become too much to handle. You have a variety of choices which we'll discuss in the next chapter.

SECTION FOUR: LATE STAGE DEMENTIA

CHAPTER NINE

Options Available to Caregivers

Decisions about caregiving are not easy or simple. In late stages of dementia, heartbreaking choices may need to be made.

If you can no longer care for your parent full-time, try not to feel guilty. You may feel like you've failed, given up, or abandoned your parent. However, remember that you'll still be caring for your parent even if it's in a different setting.

Decisions should be centered on finding the safest and healthiest option for your parent and yourself, irrespective of how or where the caregiving takes place.

You're making plenty of sacrifices to care for your parent, so don't feel guilty for getting help. Some caregivers find their relationship with their parents improve since they can concentrate on their relationship instead of the day-to-day stresses of caregiving.

Be honest with your family. This is not the time to put on a brave face or be timid. They may not realize the personal toll caregiving is taking on you. However, don't begin the discussion with a long list of complaints either. Instead, patiently explain why being the sole caregiver at home is no longer best for your parent or yourself.

Schedule a family meeting to explore and discuss all your options. If a face-to-face meeting is not feasible, use Skype or Facetime. Do your research ahead of time. Don't make hasty decisions based purely on emotions or preconceived ideas.

Be sure and discuss the financial aspect as well. Does your parent have any money saved to help with caregiving costs? Does your loved one qualify for Medicaid or veteran benefits? Can family members contribute towards the cost of caregiving?

Here are a few options you may want to consider:

IN-HOME CAREGIVING SERVICES

A wide variety of in-home caregiving services are available through health agencies or individual care providers.

Consider hiring assistance during an earlier stage of the disease. You'll have more time and energy to find the right professionals and try different agencies. If you wait too long, caregiving can become so overwhelming that you have a difficult time making the right decision.

If your parent, like my mother, protests to having a stranger around, you may be tempted to give in to your loved one's wishes. I made this mistake. During early stages of this disease, your parent may not be able to foresee future needs. Therefore, you must be the realistic one.

In the end, your parent will probably adjust easier than you imagine. Although my mother objected at first, once we hired caregivers, she adapted fairly quickly. Your parent will probably appreciate not having to bother you for every need.

You basically have two options when hiring in-home caregiving services:

- In earlier stages of the disease, you may only need non-medical companionship and supervision. If this is the case, hiring a companion will cost less than a home health aide. Services may include assistance with light housekeeping, meal preparation, and laundry.
- During later stages, you'll probably need a home health aide with specialized training. A home health aide is usually trained as a certified nursing assistant (CNA) or Patient Care Assistant (PCA). Home health aides can check vital signs and administer medication under the direction of a registered nurse or other medical professional. In addition, they can provide hands-on care such as bathing, dressing, and toilet assistance. If necessary, most services offer medical care by a licensed health professional such as a nurse at an extra cost.

Costs for home care services vary depending on services provided and where you live, but typically range from $14 to $24 an hour. If the cost is not covered by insurance, which is often the case, perhaps your parent has savings or family members can all contribute to cover the expense.

To find the right in-home service, ask your parent's primary physician as well as friends, family, and neighbors for recommendations. Join a support group to learn more about help available in your area. You can also use Medicare's online tool, Home Health Compare, to find and compare local agencies. If your parent is under hospice care, as was our case, they may be able to recommend a reliable service.

Before meeting with a prospective agency or provider, make sure they are experienced caring for dementia patients. Determine what services your parent needs and prepare questions ahead of time. For example, do their services include housekeeping and preparing meals? Are they licensed to administer medication? What will they do if your parent becomes verbally abusive, refuses to eat, or tries to wander off? Listen carefully to answers. Ask for and check references.

After you choose a service, list your parent's daily activities, habits, and preferences to make the transition easier.

When you do find a good caregiver, show your appreciation. Be sure and treat that person with the utmost respect and kindness.

ASSISTED LIVING FACILITIES

An assisted living residence provides 24-hour personal care support. Services may include meals, medication management, housekeeping, laundry, transportation, and recreational activities. Assistance with bathing and dressing is usually available if needed.

Assisted living can work well if your parent has mild cognitive problems, is mobile, and sociable. These senior communities often bridge the gap between living independently and a nursing home. If possible, choose a center that offers a dementia unit with a well-trained staff and secure environment. In some cases, a move to assisted living during earlier stages of dementia may help your parent master the new environment and make new friends while physically and mentally able to do so.

Costs vary dramatically from state to state. At the time of this writing, the average cost of assisted living nationwide was $3,700 a month. However, Alzheimer's and dementia care in assisted living usually costs an additional $1,100 per month, for a total average of $4,800 a month.

Assisted living typically costs less than a nursing home. Medicaid programs that help with the cost of assisted living and eligibility requirements vary from state to state.

NURSING HOMES

If your parent has severe cognitive impairment, incontinence, complicated medical conditions that require monitoring, or behavioral problems, you'll need to consider the increased supervision and higher staff ratios of a qualified nursing home.

These facilities usually have a licensed physician or nurse on the premises and often have physical and occupational therapists to cater to their residents' needs. Daily meals, housekeeping and laundry service, pain/medication management, hospice care, exercise and physical therapy programs, social programs and activities, and 24-hour staffing and personal assistance are typically included.

Visit several communities before choosing one. Make sure they have activities and medical support appropriate for dementia patients.

Look around to ensure the facility is clean and that the staff is friendly, available, and knowledgeable. Be clear about which services are included.

Unfortunately, unless your parent has long-term care insurance, the costs of a nursing home are substantial. The national average cost for nursing home care for a shared room averages $7,000 a month.

Medicare doesn't cover long-term care in a nursing home. Medicaid is the largest single payer for nursing home care, but individuals must meet strict financial guidelines to qualify. If your parent qualifies, however, Medicaid will pay for 100% of their nursing home costs at an approved skilled nursing facility. Veteran assistance benefit programs are also available if your parent qualifies.

PREPARING FOR ADMISSION

The move into an assisted living facility or nursing home can be an emotional transition for any parent. For those with dementia, the move is usually even more difficult. "Transfer trauma" is a term used to describe the stress that a person with dementia may experience when changing living environments.

The following are a few suggestions to help make the transition go smoother:

- If your loved one can understand and remember the reasons for the move into a facility, a discussion beforehand may be helpful.
- Visit the facility before the move to meet the administrative and nursing staff and review policies. Talk to the staff about your parent's medical history, background, medications, and any special needs.
- Create a warm, cozy, and supportive environment with familiar furniture, creature comforts, photos, artwork, flowers, books, and music to help your parent feel more secure. Prepare a list of supplies your parent will need or want to make sure you don't forget anything.

- On the day of the move, follow your parent's normal routine as much as possible and choose a time of day to move when your parent is usually at his or her best. Stay positive and avoid any arguments about the decision to move.
- Once you've arrived, *Alzheimer's A to Z: A Quick-Reference Guide*, suggests making your first visit short and sweet and keeping the conversation positive. The staff may be able to help you when it's time to leave by distracting your parent with an activity. Avoid making an emotional scene if possible.
- Be sure you have support from friends and family during this time of transition. You will probably experience a wide range of emotions including guilt, relief, and sadness, not only on the day of the move, but for weeks or months afterwards.
- Get to know the nursing staff, especially the certified nurse assistants (CNAs) who provide most the daily care. Be polite and respectful. The better you treat the staff, the better treatment your parent is likely to receive. Show your appreciation with cards, flowers, or food that everyone on the unit can enjoy.
- Since your parent may not be able to communicate well, you will need to serve as a personal ambassador to the staff. Visit often to ensure that your loved one is getting proper care and attention as well as to demonstrate your love and support. Encourage family and friends to do the same.

HOSPICE

Placing your parent in hospice may feel like you're giving up and waiting callously for your parent to die. This is not the case. Hospice allows your parent to be as comfortable as possible at home while enjoying a dignified, meaningful life in the company of loved ones. Our family found their services invaluable.

Regular visits from physicians, nurses, and home health aides assess needs and help with administering medication, managing symptoms, and controlling pain. The staff can also answer any questions you may have and coach you on how to care for your parent during the final days.

Health aides assist with bathing and dressing. The staff may also include social workers, non-denominational chaplains, and bereavement counselors to offer emotional, spiritual, and grief support.

In addition, hospice provides medication, medical supplies, and medical equipment.

Although hospice provides 24-hour-on-call access to the staff, keep in mind that they don't provide a round-the-clock caregiver and usually require that a caregiver be in the home during visits.

To begin hospice care, an individual must have a life expectancy of six months or less and a physician's referral is needed. Hospice care can be stopped at any time. If your parent lives longer than six months, hospice can usually be continued as long as needed.

Hospice care is covered by Medicare, Medicaid, and most private insurance plans. When selecting a hospice provider, make sure the agency is experienced with dementia patients.

If using Medicare benefits, keep in mind that care must be provided by a Medicare-approved hospice provider.

CHAPTER TEN

As the End Draws Near

While people can live with dementia, such as Alzheimer's or LBD for years, sadly these are terminal diseases that eventually end in death.

Signs that your parent is near the end of life may include immobility and an inability to communicate or perform daily activities such as eating or toileting. In the next chapter, we'll discuss some other signs you can expect at the end such as confusion, restlessness, a decrease in appetite, and difficulty swallowing.

Ideally, discussions about end-of-life care wishes should take place while your parent still has the capacity to make decisions and share wishes about life-sustaining treatment. In Mom's case, she had filled out an advanced healthcare directive and had expressed her fervent wishes to die at home.

I had never provided end-of-life care or even watched anyone die. Thankfully, the hospice staff guided me through the process. In addition, our family hired professional caregivers round-the-clock for the last few weeks of Mom's life. Their presence was reassuring and helped me sleep at night without fear that my mother would die alone. If at all possible, I'd recommend you have the same kind of support during this difficult time.

As I tell our story, keep in mind that everyone's experience at the end of life is different.

If your parent has not reached this stage yet, you may want to put off reading this section until your parent is showing signs that the end of life is near. This stage is painful to contemplate.

THE BEGINNING OF THE END

My husband and I were living with Mom while building a house across the street. Caregiving was extremely difficult during this time and our family was making plans to hire a professional caregiver part-time to help me. Our new home would allow me to be close by when needed.

By this time, my mother was unable to walk or get out of a chair or bed without my assistance. Nor was she able to bathe, dress, or toilet herself. Eating and drinking was becoming more difficult and incontinence was a problem. She didn't always recognize me, and hallucinations were frequent. This is typical for late-stage dementia.

Keep in mind that during this stage, death may be caused by a variety of medical complications related to dementia. For instance, because of an inability to move, those with late-stage dementia are predisposed to blood clots and bedsores. Swallowing issues may lead to an infection such as aspiration pneumonia. Difficulties with eating and drinking can contribute to weight loss or dehydration which increases vulnerability to infections. Injuries and fractures caused by falls may contribute to death.

In our case, the latter happened.

Unfortunately, falls are common for those with LBD and cannot always be avoided. Over the course of the disease, Mom had taken a few falls, but fortunately none had caused any broken bones. Since Mom could not walk or get out of a chair or bed without assistance, falls had become easier to prevent.

Or so I thought.

While my husband and I were sleeping, Mom had a frightening hallucination in the middle of the night. Evidently, an adrenaline rush allowed her to get out of bed by herself – a feat I didn't think was possible anymore – and bolt toward the door. She left her walker, which was always kept on the side of her bed, behind as she tried to "escape." My husband heard her cry out as she fell. We found her on the floor in the doorway of her bedroom.

At first, Mom was misdiagnosed with a sprained hip. We took her home as instructed, but she was unable to move without excruciating pain. We took her back to Urgent Care and a CT scan clearly detected a fractured hip which required a partial hip replacement.

We requested spinal anesthesia along with "twilight" anesthesia, as is commonly recommended for LBD patients. Fortunately, the surgeon was able to accommodate our wishes. Even so, the pain medication necessary after the surgery made my mother completely delusional. After a few days at the hospital, my Mom was sent to a rehabilitation center to recover.

My family took turns staying with her, so she was never alone during the day. Even so, unbeknownst to us, she developed a bedsore which was not detected nor treated. My knowledge of bedsores at that time was limited. I had no idea how quickly bedsores can develop and just how deadly they can be.

My youngest sister is convinced that Mom contracted a staph infection in the hospital after her surgery and that may be the case. We'll never know for sure. Regardless of the cause, as staff members were preparing my mother to go home, they discovered a seven-inch long and inch-and-a-half wide raw, gaping wound.

How this was overlooked, I cannot fathom.

STARTING HOSPICE CARE

My mother was released from the rehabilitation center and hospice care began at home. Although treatment began immediately, the sore began tunneling inward creating a sinkhole-like effect and quickly became infected. The horror began as hospice nurses probed, measured, debrided dead tissue, and packed the wound.

The medical team showed me how to roll my mother on her side to cleanse the wound, apply medication, and change the dressing in between visits.

Without any medical training and being somewhat squeamish, this task was unbearable. I am eternally grateful to my daughter-in-law, Johnni, who volunteered to take over the job while I assisted.

In the end, the wound was unresponsive to antibiotics. This is not unusual. Advanced dementia patients are often too frail, and their immune system too compromised to fight off infections, even with the assistance of drugs.

My mother began weeping as soon as we rolled her over knowing the agonizing pain that would follow. "I don't want to do this anymore," she cried pathetically.

At this point, the hospice staff let me know that my mother's situation had become hopeless. The goal now was to make her as comfortable as possible. Even without the infected wound on her back, we knew that my Mom would not survive LBD and that her time left was limited. Nonetheless, faced with the reality of her inevitable death, our family couldn't face it. We took her to the hospital one last time. A doctor told us bluntly that surgery would be excruciatingly painful and very unlikely to succeed. He strongly recommended that we bring Mom home and return her to hospice care.

I had not fully accepted that my Mom was dying until this moment. We gathered our family together and all agreed to do as recommended while crying our eyes out.

EXPRESSING LOVE IN THE FINAL DAYS

Each end is different. Death can come suddenly, or a person can linger, gradually waning. After my Mom came home from the hospital, she was placed into a hospital bed that hospice provided where she remained until her death. As my Mom's caregiver, I knew my job wasn't over yet.

Because of her dementia, my Mom never fully understood the seriousness of her disease. Now, she seemed unaware that she was dying and for that I was grateful. In my opinion, it was the only good thing about this horrific disease.

My mother was well-loved, and friends and family came and shared our tears. Even the housekeepers burst into tears when they saw her condition.

As Mom began to fade quickly, the hospice workers put in a catheter and gave her sponge baths. They also talked to us about what to expect and how we could make her as comfortable as possible.

The world is primarily experienced through a dying person's senses, they explained. Even when Mom was unable to talk or reason anymore, we could still express our love through touch, sound, sight, and smell. So, we watched old family home movies, rubbed Mom's favorite lotion into her skin, played Hawaiian music, brushed her hair, and let the sunshine warm her face. And we repeatedly expressed our love for her.

When she began to sleep most of the time, hospice workers told us that hearing is the last sense to go. With this in mind, we always kept conversations positive.

The following chapter will list some symptoms commonly experienced before death and ways you can help your parent during your final days together.

CHAPTER ELEVEN

End of Life Signs

As the end approaches, the following are some signs that your parent may be near death as well as ways to keep your loved one more comfortable. Keep in mind, end-of-life signs vary and, as with any new symptom, notify your hospice agency or the attending physician for advice and instructions. Any treatments and drugs should be based on their recommendations.

CONFUSION

Near the end, Mom was often confused and disoriented. We were advised to provide a soothing environment in a quiet, well-lit room with familiar objects and to give lots of reassurance. Since your parent may not recognize you or other family members, it's also good to clearly identify yourselves. Calmly explain any actions you are taking beforehand so your parent isn't alarmed. For example, "Now, I'm going to give you your medicine."

AGITATION

Sometimes, Mom became restless or agitated, tugging at her covers and clothing for no apparent reason.

I'M YOUR DAUGHTER, JULIE

When this happens, make sure your parent is not in pain, hungry, thirsty, or uncomfortable. Your parent may no longer be able to communicate needs or feelings verbally. Body language may be the only way your loved one can signal for help.

If you cannot find any physical reason for your parent's agitation, remember that restlessness is normal for those with dementia as well as for those in the last stages of life. Experts do not recommend restraining your loved one. Instead, try talking calmly, holding your parent's hand, or playing quiet music.

A BURST OF ENERGY

This doesn't always happen, but sometimes a loved one close to death will temporarily have a surge of energy and become more alert.

If you are lucky enough to get this time, be sure and take full advantage of the moment.

Right before we began morphine treatments, shockingly, my Mom became more alert than she had been in weeks. "This feels like a party," she said after noticing her sister-in-law and an old friend were visiting.

She asked to put on her favorite red lipstick and rings and wanted a sip of wine. We happily granted every wish. My mother talked about taking a trip to Maui together and we played Hawaiian music in the background. Later that day, Mom went to sleep feeling content.

That was the last time we were able to have a meaningful conversation with her. It was as if Mom briefly came back to life to say her good-byes.

But for that moment in time, family members and friends had a last chance to tell her how much we loved her. Not everyone has the opportunity to do that and for that precious gift, I am grateful.

LOSS OF APPETITE AND INTEREST IN FLUIDS

Losing one's appetite is a common and normal part of dying. Swallowing typically becomes difficult as well. You can try offering your parent's favorite foods and easy-to-eat soft foods in small amounts if your loved one is too weak to eat. The time usually comes, however, when your parent will refuse food. Despite our instincts, we were instructed not to force Mom to eat when this happened. Experts say that the effort required to eat, digest, and eliminate is often too much for a dying person's body to handle.

In an effort to prolong life, you may be tempted to use a feeding tube. Although this is a personal choice that should be based on your parent's attending physician's recommendations, according to the National Institute on Aging, tube feeding does not prolong life or prevent aspiration in those with dementia and can cause even more discomfort. The American Geriatrics Society and the Alzheimer's Association also do not recommend feeding tubes for older adults with advanced dementia.

Resisting fluids is also part of the natural process. According to studies, a reduction of fluids can reduce nausea, vomiting, bloating, and diarrhea as well as decrease the amount of fluid buildup in the lungs. Hospice advised us to use a sponge on a stick dipped in water to relieve dehydration. Lip balm and ice chips can help parched lips and a dry mouth.

SHORTNESS OF BREATH AND RATTLING

Rattling sounds, which can be quite loud, may occur as the end nears. Healthy people can normally clear their own throat, swallow, or spit out any excess secretions. At the end of life, however, your parent may be too weak to do so.

According to Healthline, "No evidence currently suggests that a death rattle is painful, distracting, or distressing to the dying person." The noise will probably be more disturbing to you than to your parent. Suctioning, which can increase secretions and discomfort, is not usually recommended.

Your parent's physician or hospice may suggest drugs to help dry up excess secretions, which can help clear up the death rattle. Turning your parent to one side or elevating your parent's head may also help lessen or stop the rattling, according to many experts.

Your parent may also stop breathing for a few seconds or experience periods of rapid, shallow panting. Sometimes, as part of hospice or palliative care, morphine or other pain medications are administered to help relieve the sense of breathlessness.

CHAPTER TWELVE

The End of The Journey

Hospice nurses predicted that Mom would probably die in three to seven days. People can hover between life and death for hours and even days. Therefore, death can be hard to predict, and it can be easy to miss the final moment. In our case, however, their estimate proved to be accurate.

MORPHINE TREATMENTS

Morphine and similar drugs are often used in hospice and palliative care to relieve severe pain and maintain comfort and quality of life as a patient approaches death. Of course, any drugs should be administered or monitored by trained staff.

In our case, our hospice team recommended oral morphine treatment to control the excruciating pain in my Mom's back from the tunneling wound and ease her through the dying process. I was given detailed instructions on how to correctly administer the proper dosages of morphine. Doses were increased gradually as needed as her body started to shut down.

At first, when I gave Mom morphine, it felt like I was hastening her death. A hospice nurse assured me this was not the case.

"Most experts think this [morphine leading to a quicker death] is unlikely, especially if increasing the dose is done carefully," according to NIH's site. "Successfully reducing pain and/or concerns about breathing can provide needed comfort to someone who is close to dying".

THE LAST BREATH

On day six, our caregiver told me that my mother had a weak pulse. Mom also began a pattern of breathing – commonly known as Cheyne-Stokes – breathing periodically, followed by no breath for several seconds, followed by another intake of breath.

After almost a week of agonizing waiting, he warned me that my Mom would likely die within the next two hours. We immediately called my sisters so they could come to the house. My father, my brother, my husband, and I were all there and expressed our love for Mom and told her how much she meant to us. We promised that we would all take care of each other after she was gone.

I gently kissed Mom's face one last time. Since we share the same faith, I told her that as a loyal servant of God she would be safe under His care and I looked forward to seeing her again when she would not be in pain or sick anymore.

My youngest son and his wife came in to say their good-byes. I went into the living room to check on my father and talk to the caregiver. When I returned to Mom's bedroom, the pauses between her breaths were much longer. She appeared calm and comfortable.

And then she took her last breath. When the actual death occurs, it happens very quickly.

TAKE TIME FOR FINAL GOOD-BYES

You may feel a profound sadness at the time of death, simply numb, or relieved your parent is no long suffering. Death may even feel impersonal or anti-climactic, especially if you're in a hospital or nursing home where staff is coming in and out to deal with necessary procedures. There is no right or wrong way to feel.

Everyone is comforted in different ways. Remember, there is no rush after your parent dies. The caregiver discreetly gave us time alone with Mom's body after she died. If your parent dies in a facility, you can ask any present staff to do the same.

Some people find this time unexpectedly peaceful while others don't wish to stay with the body. Do whatever brings you comfort.

In our case, my two sisters and brother-in-law arrived a few moments after Mom's death. They were at peace with the fact since everyone had ample time for good-byes. Our family sat in the room with our mother for a while and cried together. We all gave her our final hugs and kisses.

Afterwards, we called the hospice nurse who came to care for Mom's body. Our family went outside on the patio. We looked at the stars and talked about some of our cherished memories. Surprisingly, we were even able to laugh about some of the humorous moments we had with Mom.

However, when the mortuary came to take my mother away, we all burst into tears again. Grief came in tidal waves of despair.

SECTION FIVE: AFTER YOUR LOVED ONE DIES

CHAPTER THIRTEEN

How to Move Forward

As anyone who has lost a parent knows, grieving is a journey. There are no shortcuts to the healing process. Unless we die first, losing our parents is a road we must all travel.

No doubt, watching a parent die will have a profound effect on you.

"The reality is that you will grieve forever," psychiatrist and author Elisabeth Kübler-Ross wrote. "You will not 'get over' the loss of a loved one; you will learn to live with it. You will heal and you will rebuild yourself around the loss you have suffered. You will be whole again but you will never be the same. Nor should you be the same nor would you want to."

My heart goes out to all of you caregivers who face the anguish of watching your loved one suffer and then die from dementia.

Be kind and gentle on yourselves as you begin to heal and rebuild your life.

After my Mom died, the parade of relatives and friends coming through the house was exhausting, but also a blessing of sorts. All the people were a distraction and not entirely unwelcome since my emotions would have been overwhelming if I was alone. Family, friends, and members of our congregation offered kind words, hugs, and prayers which was comforting.

But, eventually, I was forced to deal with all my feelings.

Surprisingly, amidst all the pain, I could still feel grateful. Some people lose a parent while still young, but I had the privilege of spending most my life with Mom who was almost 78 when she died. I was thankful for my loving husband, children, and grandchildren as well as a large, close-knit family that supported me through this difficult time.

And I was grateful for my faith that taught me to rely on God for strength and gave me the comforting assurance that I would see my Mom again.

Still, my heart broke into a million pieces.

Healing was especially difficult since other stressful events were occurring at the same time. My mother-in-law was dying from ovarian cancer. My oldest son was going through a horrible divorce and custody battle. The new house we had built to be closer to my Mom – who unfortunately died the week before it was finished – was finally ready which required the demanding process of moving. Since I was forced to give up my larger clients as a freelance writer to provide caregiving, I needed to find some new projects quickly to help pay for the mortgage.

Between grieving and all the traumatic and heartbreaking events in my life, I was shaken, fragile, vulnerable, exhausted, and depressed.

How do you move forward after a life-changing event? How do you pick up the scattered pieces of your soul and begin living again?

Here are seven steps I found essential:

ACCEPT YOUR FEELINGS

My feelings were all over the place after my mother died. After the numbness wore off, I felt an overwhelming sorrow.

Instead of a lifetime of happy recollections of when my mother was healthy, memories of my Mom suffering and taking her last breath tormented me. All the times I wasn't the perfect caregiver filled me with remorse. I questioned whether right decisions were made along the way.

On top of these emotions, I felt lost. Caring for Mom had been my life for a few years. Most of my thoughts and feelings had revolved around her care. I not only lost my mother, but part of my identity as a caregiver. My role had changed drastically overnight. Who was I? I certainly didn't feel like the same person anymore.

At the same time, I felt relieved. Mom was no longer suffering and my demanding and heartbreaking duties as a caregiver were over. No more medical emergencies, constant worrying, and sleepless nights. Of course, I enjoyed my newfound freedom to take a vacation, go on a leisurely walk, spend quiet time with my husband, or simply enjoy a book. But there was guilt mixed in for feeling this way.

All these intense and contradictory feelings are normal and part of the process.

Your experience and emotions may be entirely different. For example, maybe you had a difficult relationship with your parent that was full of disappointment, betrayal, or conflict. In that case, you may be grieving the relationship you wished you had with your parent.

Or maybe you simply feel lethargic, confused, depressed, or angry. Whether you like it or not, you'll be forced to go along for this bumpy, painful ride complete with all the ups and downs.

I'll discuss how to find yourself again and move forward later. For now, acknowledge all your feelings instead of sweeping them under a rug. Be patient with yourself. Accept and honor the journey. Feel what you need to feel.

LEAN ON LOVED ONES

Although it's tempting, now is not the time to isolate yourself or try to appear brave. The people who love you want to help. Let them.

I'm an introvert by nature and a private person. Even though it didn't come naturally, I openly and honestly discussed my thoughts and feelings with those who loved me. Doing so helped me decide what to do next and figure out how to move forward with my life.

If you have and are close to your siblings, they are traveling the same painful journey and experiencing similar emotions. Losing a parent can strengthen your bonds so you don't feel alone as you grieve. Perhaps you lost contact with friends while you were caregiving. Now is the time to reconnect. Allow them to help you heal.

If you're a spiritual person, this is the time to strengthen your relationship with God, so he can give you the power to carry on and find inner peace again. For me, healing meant lots of heartfelt prayer.

FOCUS ON YOURSELF

Take the time you need to focus on all your needs – physically, emotionally, and spiritually.

Since many caregivers neglect their health, this is the perfect time to take control. In my case, it had been four years since I had a check-up – not a good thing in your mid-50s. Unfortunately, I had been stress eating and weighed in over 170 pounds, moving ever closer to obesity. A doctor's visit and mammogram were in order. I began my journey to eat healthier, lose 20 pounds, and exercise on a regular basis. I immediately felt better.

Emotionally and spiritually, I deemed the time after Mom's death as my "year of healing" with a list of three non-negotiable things I had to do each and every day. There wasn't anything revolutionary or new on my list. Just three simple things that provided an anchor and helped me get through a bad day.

My list included:

#1: Read something spiritual or inspirational every single day. I am a regular Bible reader. Even so, I'd become sidetracked with work and the business of life and a day or two would slip by without any spiritual fortification. I realized daily reading, meditation, and prayer were necessary every day.

#2: Exercise. Yes, I was exercising as part of my attempt to lose weight, but not every day. Even if it was only 15 minutes, I did something for both my physical and emotional well-being. Some days I went to the park and walked. Other days, I followed a relaxing 20-minute Windsor Pilates routine on YouTube. Most days, my dog sat by my shoes in the closet begging me with his sad eyes, successfully guilting me into taking him for a walk around the block.

#3: Do something I love to refuel and refresh myself, so my tank was not depleted. Maybe I'd lounge on the couch by a fire with popcorn and read a bestseller. Or I'd sit on the patio with a glass of wine, relaxing music, and watch the sunset with hubby. On a stressful day, I might do some deep breathing or write in my journal. The activities varied, but at the end of the day, I made sure that I did something just for me.

You know what? My list worked. I felt calmer, more centered, and yes, happier. I'd highly recommend making a similar list. Although it's tempting to list 10 things you should do every day, I'd suggest starting with just three to put less pressure on yourself.

Everyone's list will be different. Maybe you'll include spending time in nature, learning something new, being silly, or spending time with loved ones each and every day.

Just make the commitment and get started on your path to healing.

MOVE FORWARD

Of course, you'll never stop missing your parent. Grieving is inevitable, so take the time you need to mourn. But don't allow sorrow to become a way of life. Be careful not to get stuck in all the "I should have..." or "I wish..." that often comes with the territory but can interfere with your recovery. Forgive yourself for mistakes you think were made while caregiving.

The goal is not to wallow forever in negative feelings but to move on, be there for the people who need you, and enjoy life once again.

Remember, no one is immune from painful experiences in life. If I can leave you with one positive thought, it is that you can survive anything. No matter what adversities you face, you can regain your footing, take a deep breath, and move forward. You can make a conscious decision to make the most of your life.

Focusing on the needs of others is an effective and positive way to move forward. Helping people make it through their own grief, simple acts of kindness and compassion, and volunteer work can help you find meaning and purpose again.

The fact is that most of us don't grieve around the clock for the rest of our lives. Life goes on and takes us with it. Our ability and infinite capacity to endure and bounce back is far greater than we think.

Keep moving forward and, with time, your memories of your parent will change from painful recollections of your loved one's illness and death to all the cherished, happy times you spent together. You'll appreciate that the experience of caregiving helped you grow as a person in ways that otherwise would not be possible. After all, you developed strength, endurance, and empathy that will benefit you for the rest of your life.

There is light at the end of the tunnel, I promise.

REDISCOVER YOURSELF

After Mom died, I wasn't sure what was "normal" anymore. Did I even want the same things?

While caregiving, you no doubt gave up things you enjoyed and lost a bit of yourself. Your life changed drastically and, without a doubt, you're not the same person. Now is the time to get to know yourself again and perhaps make some changes.

Actually, when something bad happens, it can be a potent and powerful influence. The experience can clarify your priorities and redefine your path. So, embrace the new you and your new life.

For example, I went back to freelance writing after Mom died. But after decades of stressful deadlines, I wanted more creative control over my career. Specifically, I wanted to decide what to write and how much time I spent doing it. So, I started my journey to independence with a blog and a few book projects.

Now it's your turn. What do you want to change? What truly makes you happy? What really matters to you? How can you best use your qualities and skills? What is it that will make you excited to get out of bed every day? What brings fun and joy to your life?

Discover what kind of action will make you feel fulfilled and make a list of what you can do to reach your goals. Then, each day, take one small step toward that goal.

You'll go through several stages before this happens, but eventually you'll discover all the possibilities that a major change in life offers. In time, you'll reconnect with old friends or make new friends, go to work or back to school, volunteer, enjoy new adventures, and rediscover yourself along the way.

APPRECIATE EACH DAY OF LIFE

Losing a loved one will change how you look at the world and force you to acknowledge that life does not last forever. As a result, you often appreciate more fully every day of life you are granted.

Use this newfound appreciation.

Refuse to settle for less than you deserve, waste time on negative people, or hold on to bad memories.

Take note of all the small, ordinary moments that make each day special. Cherish the laugh of a child, a hug from a friend, the sound of a bird singing, or the smells after a rainstorm. Savor the first spring day in your garden, the kindness of a stranger, or that first sip of coffee.

Live life to the fullest and get out of your comfort zone. Maybe that means traveling to a new place, trying a new sport, changing your hair, or taking classes. What scares you a little? Go for it and shake things up a little.

Your parent would want all these things for you.

TAKE THAT FIRST STEP

Several months after Mom died, my husband and I took an anniversary trip to Chicago. Even though I have a fear of heights, I was determined to sit on one of those scary glass enclosures that jut from the Willis Tower's Skydeck, a whopping 103 floors above the city.

Suddenly, I had this overwhelming feeling that I had to start living again and this was the first step. So, I bravely forged forward onto the glass. And I felt alive, empowered, and revitalized.

I have faith that you'll take that first step too. You will heal, move forward, and rediscover yourself. You will feel happy again.

As Martin Luther King Jr. famously said, "Take the first step in faith. You don't have to see the whole staircase, just take the first step."

AFTERWORD

I'm Your Daughter, Julie was written out of a sincere desire to help other family caregivers. If you found this book useful, you can help me get the word out to other caregivers by writing a short review on Amazon. Even just a line or two can make a big difference.

I'd be delighted to hear from you. You can connect with me on my website, blog, or social media sites:

Visit my website at www.juliegorges.com

Follow me on Facebook at www.facebook.com/julieagorges

Follow me on Twitter at www.twitter.com/JulieGorges

Visit my Amazon author's page at www.amazon.com/author/juliegorges

Visit my blog at www.babyboomerbliss.net

RESOURCES

The Internet is a source of extensive and free information on dementia and how to care of people with the disease. The following are some useful websites you may want to check out:

The Alzheimer's Association: www.alz.org
The Alzheimer's Association Caregiver Center: www.alz.org/care
The Association of Frontotemporal Degeneration: www.theaftd.org
Dementia Care Central: www.dementiacarecentral.com
Family Caregiver Alliance: www.caregiver.org/about-fca
Lewy Body Dementia Association: www.lbda.org
The National Institute on Aging: www.nia.nih.gov/health/caregiving
The National Association for Home Care and Hospice (NAHC): www.nahc.org

GLOSSARY

A

Agitation. Extreme restlessness and anxiety, which can result in pacing, fidgeting, and difficulty sleeping in those with dementia.

Alzheimer's. The most common type of dementia with early symptoms that include memory and vocabulary problems, confusion, disorientation, poor judgement. Symptoms in later stages may include agitation, sleep disturbances, delusions, anger, paranoia, urinary incontinence, difficulty walking and speaking, and verbal or physical outbursts.

Antipsychotic Medications. Sometimes prescribed for those with Alzheimer's but to be used with extreme caution. Recent research has shown that these drugs are associated with an increased risk of stroke and death in older adults with dementia.

Assisted Living. An assisted living residence provides 24-hour personal care support. Services may include meals, medication management, housekeeping, laundry, transportation, and recreational activities. Assistance with bathing and dressing is usually available if needed.

B

Bed Sores. Sometimes called pressure ulcers and decubitus ulcers, these injuries to skin and underlying tissue are caused by poor circulation due to prolonged pressure on body parts. Although preventable, these sometimes-life-threatening sores are a danger to bedridden or immobile patients.

Behavior and Personality Changes. Symptoms that worsen as dementia progresses that may include behavioral issues such as wandering, paranoia, embarrassing conduct, and aggression.

C

Caregiver. A person who provides direct care, as referenced in this book, for those with dementia.

Certified Nursing Assistants (CNA). Trained and certified home health aides often employed by in-home caregiving services. Sometimes referred to as Patient Care Assistants (PCA), they can check vital signs and administer medication under the direction of a registered nurse or other medical professional. In addition, a home health aide can provide hands-on care such as bathing, dressing, and toilet assistance.

Cholinesterase Inhibitors. An FDA approved medication used to delay or slow worsening of Alzheimer's symptoms. Effectiveness varies from person to person.

Cognitive Decline. Mild cognitive decline can range from the normal decline of aging and the more serious impairment of dementia. Typically, cognitive impairment involves problems with memory, language, thinking, and poor judgment.

Cognitive Testing. Testing to assess thinking abilities including memory, language, attention span, and problem-solving. This test is often used to determine if a patient has dementia.

Creutzfeldt-Jakob Disease. A rare, fatal brain disorder that impairs memory and coordination and causes behavior changes.

D

Delusions. A false but strong belief in something that isn't real.

Dementia. A blanket term that describes symptoms that affect memory, judgement, language, and motor skills.

Disorientation. Mental confusion often experienced by those suffering with dementia, especially regarding location, time, date, or personal identity.

E

Early Stage Dementia. During early stage dementia, symptoms may include memory loss, increasing confusion especially regarding time and place, difficulty performing normal tasks, vocabulary problems, and trouble concentrating. A doctor may be able to detect cognitive problems during a patient interview and exam during this stage.

F

Frontotemporal dementia. A type of dementia known for changes in personality and behavior as well as difficulty with language.

H

Hallucinations. A sensory experience of something that does not exist outside the mind, usually manifested as visual or auditory images.

Home Health Aide. A trained and certified health-care worker that assists with personal care and sometimes light household duties. Home health aides may also monitor a patient's condition.

Hospice Care. A service, typically home-based, that supports patients and caregivers during the final phase of dementia focusing on comfort and quality of life.

Huntington's Disease. A kind of dementia known for abnormal involuntary movements, a severe decline in thinking and reasoning skills, irritability, depression and other mood changes.

I

In-Home Caregiving Services. Agencies that provide trained caregivers who provide in-home support services. These agencies typically offer a wide range of services, from preparing meals and light housework to simply providing companionship. Trained home health aides can also monitor patients and assist with daily care such as bathing, dressing, and going to the toilet.

L

Lewy Body Dementia (LBD). The second most common type of dementia. Symptoms include memory problems, confusion, difficulty concentrating, disorientation, paranoia, agitation, emotional distress, urinary incontinence, anxiety, depression. Those with LBD often experience vivid and intense hallucinations, night terrors, and delusions in addition to Parkinson-like symptoms such as tremors, rigid muscles, stooped posture, and balance problems.

M

Magnetic Resonance Imaging (MRI). Often used to eliminate other causes of mental decline such as a stroke, brain tumors, or blood clots in the brain.

Memantine. An FDA approved drug that improves mental function and ability to perform daily activities for some people with Alzheimer's.

Mixed Dementia. When more than one type of dementia occurs simultaneously in the brain.

N

Namzaric. The combination of cholinesterase inhibitors and memantine, drugs that may temporarily lessen and stabilize cognitive symptoms including memory loss, confusion, and problems with thinking and reasoning.

Normal Pressure Hydrocephalus. A type of dementia with symptoms that include difficulty walking, memory loss and inability to control urination.

Neurologist. Specializes in diagnosing and treating disorders of the nervous system, including diseases of the brain, nerves, and muscles such as dementia, strokes, and Parkinson's.

P

Paranoia. An unfounded distrust of others, sometimes reaching a delusional state. Those with dementia often wrongly suspect the motives of others, think others are stealing valuables, or believe that individuals mean them harm.

Parkinson's Disease. This disease often results in progressive dementia and typically involves problems with movement.

Patient Care Assistants (PCA). See Certified Nursing Assistants (CNA).

Pre-Dementia. This stage of slight cognitive decline is associated with normal forgetfulness that often comes with aging.

R

REM Sleep Disorders. Instead of experiencing the normal temporary paralysis of arms and legs, those with this disorder physically act out dreams. A common symptom of LBD, an individual exhibits vocalizations and/or complex motor behaviors (running, punching, jumping) while they are in a REM state of sleep.

S

Sundowning. A term used for dementia patients who become restless or agitated in the late afternoon or early evening, often causing behavior problems late into the night.

T

Transfer Techniques. Proper methods to transfer a dementia patient in and out of bed or on and off a chair, toilet, or wheelchair.

U

Urinary Incontinence. The loss of bladder control that often accompanies dementia in late stages.

V

Vascular Dementia. This type of dementia accounts for about 10 percent of dementia cases and is a result of brain injuries and inadequate blood flow. Typically, symptoms include confusion, disorientation, speech problems, vision loss, and a lack of ability to make decisions or plans.

W

Wandering. A term used when dementia patients wander, get lost, and become disoriented even in familiar places.

Wernicke-Korsakoff Syndrome. A type of dementia recognized for its severe memory problems often connected to alcohol misuse.

INDEX

Made in the USA
San Bernardino, CA
10 March 2019